THE
PERSONALITY
OF THE
ALCOHOLIC

GUISES OF
DEPENDENCY

by Howard T. Blane

Associate Psychologist,
Massachusetts General Hospital

Assistant Clinical Professor
of Psychology,
Harvard Medical School

This searchlight on the alcoholic personality illuminates significant traits so that the relatively untrained person in daily contact with an alcoholic can better understand and help him. Dr. Blane describes characteristics and behavior that occur in alcoholics with enough frequency to warrant ascribing a certain degree of generality to them. But that there is no such thing as a specific personality particular to all alcoholics and to them alone, this book clearly demonstrates also.

(continued on back flap)

THE PERSONALITY
OF THE ALCOHOLIC

To John Taylor
with regards
and warm
wishes
Howard C
Blane 1987

THE PERSONALITY
OF THE ALCOHOLIC
Guises of Dependency

by Howard T. Blane, Ph.D.

Associate Psychologist,
Massachusetts General Hospital

Assistant Clinical Professor of Psychology,
Harvard Medical School

1817

HARPER & ROW, PUBLISHERS
NEW YORK, EVANSTON, AND LONDON

LIBRARY OF CONGRESS CATALOG CARD NUMBER: 67-22523

To Eleanor

CONTENTS

THE PERSONALITY
OF THE ALCOHOLIC

1

INTRODUCTION

A WORK ABOUT the personality of the alcoholic for the general reader has never been written. The need for such a book is revealed by a casual reading of Sunday supplements and the so-called women's magazines, with their efflorescence of simple and misleading stories about alcoholics. There is an observable regularity in the appearance of magazine articles, comic strip series, television shows, and radio serials on alcohol, its use and abuse, alcoholics, and alcoholism. Less infrequent, but more enduring accounts, like Charles Jackson's *The Lost Weekend,* Eugene O'Neill's plays, notably *The Iceman Cometh* and *Long Day's Journey Into Night,* and J. P. Miller's *Days of Wine and Roses,* are unsurpassed portraits of the inner experience of individual alcoholics.

What do such accounts tell us of the personality of the alcoholic? Very little and yet a great deal. A large number of the manifold communications that appear almost daily can be dismissed on the grounds of superficiality or sensationalism. Another group, seemingly dealing with what alcoholics are like, focus melodramatically on the external predicaments in which alcoholics typically find themselves as a consequence of drinking. These include the embarrassment of the family when guests arrive during one of Father's bouts, the alcoholic's pathetic ingenuity in hiding and hoarding his supply of alcohol, the threatened loss of the job, and the sordid history of the gradual erosion and final dissolution of a marriage. These accounts, while they may include graphic portrayals of guilt and remorse, tell us little about the alcoholic as a person. A small number of stories, plays, and novels tell us a great deal about alcoholics; they often contain insights difficult to categorize in any hard and fast way. I recommend them to any serious student of alcoholism: they are provocative, intuitive, and at their best a never-failing source of new meaning. It is unfortunate that the subtlety and depth of these works do not permit us to organize their idiosyncratic insights into easily communicable form. They must be taken for what they are, works of art, creations transcending ordinary experience, and so not directly amenable to scientific scrutiny. Their insights may be invaluable to science, but cannot be a substitute for it.

What about the scientific and professional literature on the personality of the alcoholic? The situation here both parallels and differs from what we observe in the popular scene. While the man in the street seems able and almost too willing to air his views about alcoholics, many who work with them professionally are more constrained and less certain. The unrelieved solemnity of the scholarly journal replaces the racy drama of the newspaper column, and the ponderous caution of the former often obfuscates the superficiality it shares with the latter: both may have equally little to say about the alcoholic as a person. Fictional but essentially literary accounts, like those of O'Neill, Jackson, and Miller, also find their parallel or, perhaps more correctly, their reflection in occasional case studies which reveal a satisfying faculty for combining theory and intuition in just the right blend. Despite professional reluctance to commit oneself to a definable point of view, vociferous assertions that start teapot controversies do occur. Subsequent disagreements are usually less substantial than real, arising from differing definitions of terms, ambiguous semantics, or niceties of theoretical viewpoints. It is no accident that I make the professional literature on the alcoholic resemble a potpourri, for it is a mixture containing the best and the worst, the most tendentious and the most detached, the most obscure and the most lucid of scientific writing. Without doing the literature too great a violence, one may extract from this conglomerate two kinds of technical article that have dealt seriously and influentially with the personality of the alcoholic.

The first type is written by the practitioner who directs his professional activity toward problem drinkers who come to him for treatment. His articles, usually based on one of the various and slightly differing psychoanalytic theories, are intended to describe some aspect of the personality structure of the alcoholic, based on experience with a number of alcoholic patients. He tends to seek events or constellations of events in the individual's early life history that form sufficient and necessary grounds for subsequent difficulties with alcohol. Often the language is technical and requires careful knowledge of theory, so that the lay reader at best finds it difficult to follow. Disregarding academic doctrinal differences among authors, one finds substantial agreement as to what alcoholics are like. True, one writer may argue that self-destructive forces are the primary organizing factor, while a second opts for conflict over dependent wishes, but both see aggressive *and* dependent impulses as important aspects of the alcoholic's personality. None has ever presented an over-all description of traits that characterize alcoholics or attempted to present them in such a way that the relatively untrained person who has daily contact with alcoholics can use his reading to understand and to help the individual. These articles are, nevertheless, of considerable importance, for they show that there are personality characteristics and consistent patterns of behavior common to alcoholics.

The second type of technical article is written by the research scientist, who attempts to measure regularities in nature while taking into account extraneous influence. In studies of personality factors among alcoholics, he has usually been either a psychologist or a sociologist. The general procedure these investigators follow is to measure a personality factor or set of factors in a group of alcoholics and, also, in a group of nonalcoholics, and then to assess the degree of difference, if any, between the two groups. The findings obtained in such investigations were reviewed and summarized in 1950 by Edwin Sutherland, a sociologist, and his colleagues, and again in 1957 by Leonard Syme, also a sociologist.* Both reviews conclude that evidence is insufficient to indicate that there is such a thing as the personality of the alcoholic!

These two reviews have had an extremely unfortunate influence on professional views regarding personality factors among alcoholics. Many persons whose daily work is with alcoholics take the conclusions of these reviews as final and inviolable laws and say, "If there is no alcoholic personality, let's forget about the whole question." As a result, the research scientist has tended until recently not to undertake studies involving personality factors among alcoholics, while the practicing clinician has hesitated to air his insights in the professional press, even though his therapeutic contacts with individual problem drinkers definitely presuppose some coherent though perhaps implicit body of assumptions about the psychological functioning of his alcoholic clients. All this means that there has been a definite stunting of knowledge of a crucial aspect of alcoholism.

Why was it that these influential reviews came to the conclusion that they did? There is no denying that most of the studies they surveyed failed to meet minimal scientific standards. This simply means, however, that their results cannot be employed either to support or refute a notion that says that alcoholics are different from nonalcoholics with respect to personality features. Inadequately done research with contradictory findings ignores a mass of evidence—anecdotal, autobiographical, and clinical—that con-

* For Bibliographic Notes for all chapters see pages 165–167.

sistently shows that the personality characteristics of alcoholics are qualitatively different from those of their nonalcoholic brethren. Sutherland and his group, and later Syme, accepted the idea of a personality structure *unique* to alcoholics and *to alcoholics only.* They set it up as a straw man and then proceeded to knock it down.

We now end up with two paradoxes. The mass media tell us nothing and yet tell us everything about the personality of the alcoholic. The experts in alcoholism say that there is no personality of the alcoholic and that there are regularly observed personality patterns among alcoholics. I aim to bring some order to a chaotic situation and at the same time to portray this order so that the reader will find it useful, informative, and a basis for action.

Let me begin by stating that this book is not to be taken as *the* personality portrait of every alcoholic. There is no such thing as a specific personality unique to *all* alcoholics and to no other group of persons. The assumption that there is such a personality has been made not only for alcoholism, but also for a host of other conditions, so that we have had the ulcer personality, the asthmatic personality, and so on, each specific to its own illness. This view is now largely out of psychiatric fashion, although twenty or thirty years ago it enjoyed considerable popularity. And it still has a fascination for many. A bit of reflection, and this view quickly runs into difficulty; for instance, how do we conceive the personality of an alcoholic who also has an ulcer? Does he have two personalities simultaneously, or does he have an alcoholic personality when he is drinking and an ulcer personality during ulcer pain, and what of the situation when he is drinking and having ulcer pain at the same time? Mischievous questions like these have their serious side. If we hold to the conception that the architecture of adult personality is relatively stable and enduring, then it is absurdly whimsical, however delightful, to consider personalities that change their form according to what a person is doing at the moment, or to contemplate the simultaneous existence in one individual of two personalities. The three faces of Eve do occur, but not at the same time.

The traits I describe are those that have most forcibly come to my attention or to the attention of others. I feel, nonetheless, that they permit me to draw a series of high-lighted portraits of alcoholics. And here the subtleties so beautifully delineated by the creative artist offer me invaluable help.

Finally, I do not take it upon myself to offer a scheme of the causes of alcoholism. This has been attempted many times and from many viewpoints, and the cause or causes of alcoholism remain as much a mystery today as they were a hundred or a thousand years ago. Nor do I hold any brief for personality features as carrying the primary responsibility for the development of alcoholism. As a psychologist, I write about what I am most intimately familiar with and about what makes my professional life meaningful: the understanding of people. Nonetheless, the roots of alcoholism may some day be found in our physical structure or in our social system. The most commonly held contemporary notion about what causes alcoholism is that it is a product of multiple influences that derive not only from personal-historical sources, but from physiological, social, and cultural influences as well. The careful reader may remark at this point that this is merely an elaborate way of saying we don't know what causes alcoholism; but we do know quite a bit about some of the terms of this admittedly hedged formulation. For example, we know that alcoholism is almost nonexistent among Jews and Chinese, but has a high incidence among the Irish and Scandinavians. Another example is that alcoholics frequently have alcoholic fathers; it is obvious, though, that not all alcoholic fathers have alcoholic children. However, we know relatively little about precisely why and how an individual becomes alcoholic, and the several theories of etiology lack conviction both theoretically and in light of observations that contradict or otherwise fail to support them.

INTRODUCTION

My primary intention in this book is to describe behaviors and characteristics often seen in my experience, often seen in that of my colleagues and students, or described by others as occurring in alcoholics with enough frequency to indicate a high degree of regularity. The traits discussed are not centrally present in all alcoholics, but are common enough to merit attention. Nor are they of equal intensity; that is, the patterning and organization of the traits vary from individual to individual. Further, all of these traits are seen in persons who are not alcoholic; indeed, if we examine ourselves we are apt to see them, the difference being that they are transitory, that they are not vitally important to us, that they do not rule us to the point where they prevent us from doing what we want to do or make us do what we do not want to do, and, finally, that they are woven smoothly into the ebb and flow of our inner requirements so that they assist rather than hinder us in attaining day-to-day and long-range goals. In a sentence, they tend not to cause us conflict, as they so often do in the alcoholic.

My second aim is to discuss these traits in ways that will help those of you who work directly or peripherally with alcoholics or their wives, parents, children, or other relatives; physicians, nurses, and members of other paramedical professions; psychologists and social workers; clergymen, educators, and personnel officers; policemen, correctional workers, and welfare officials; and, finally, and hardly least, the problem drinker himself. The actions and attitudes of alcoholics are often confusing, contradictory, disturbing, or provocative to others. My portrayal of the personality of the alcoholic will, hopefully, offer some understanding of the ways in which alcoholics behave and some of the reasons behind these ways of behaving.

Two key terms require definition: personality and alcoholism. Personality is a patterned cluster of traits or characteristics whose expression internally (in fantasy, dreams, and thoughts) and externally (in motoric action) flows and ebbs with circumstance. One, or sometimes more, of these traits serves a central organizing role that colors or sets the tone for the rest. The traits and their patterning or organization develop in rudimentary form early in life and set the basic pattern for the years that follow. The traits themselves may be viewed as compromises between our early wishes to do exactly what we please and the dictates of the society in which we live. Technically, this definition of personality reflects an eclectic position that borrows from Freud and other psychoanalytic writers, from Gordon Allport and from Kurt Lewin.

This descriptive definition is useful when I see a person in treatment. It tells me to look for central traits, the ways that they developed in early life, and, most importantly, the nature of the compromises between wishes and reality. Where the compromise is tenuous, rigid, poorly organized, and unsatisfying to the individual, one can expect signs of conflict. These signs may include many things: tension, anxiety, or outright formation of painful and disturbing symptoms. Often, it includes the development of a pattern of behavior that is seemingly comfortable for the individual (although intensive examination of the person's feelings proves this not to be the case) but disturbing to those around him.

Now let me define the term alcoholic. No one has yet come up with an entirely satisfying definition that would tell us, so that all would agree, who is and who is not an alcoholic. The lack of a satisfactory definition of alcoholism does not disturb the person who works daily with problem drinkers, since he deals with persons who come to him either with a self-identified problem with alcohol or who are referred as alcoholic by another individual or agency. The scientist, on the other hand, is sorely troubled at being unable to make a clear-cut statement about who is and who is not alcoholic, or having to choose somewhat arbitrarily among several possible definitions, for his definition can affect his findings. This is a particularly severe problem for the scientist who wishes to determine the frequency of all persons who are alcoholic at a given time or who wishes to count the number of new cases of alcoholism that occur within a given time. Lacking a satisfactory definition of alcoholism, he has difficulty in discovering the cases that exist in a community. He can manage to count those cases that appear forcibly, or otherwise, before the public eye; that is, persons who seek treatment at public agencies for a drinking problem or those incarcerated for drunkenness. But he needs a careful definition before he can design techniques to identify hidden, nonpublic problem drinkers in the community.

The most commonly espoused definition is one proposed by Mark Keller, following that adopted by the World Health Organization. This definition states that:

Alcoholism is a chronic behavioral disorder manifested by repeated drinking of alcoholic beverages in excess of the dietary and social uses of the community and to an extent that interferes with the drinker's health or his social or economic functioning.

This is a comprehensive statement; unfortunately, it is so general that the investigator finds no easy way of translating it into concrete terms. What, for example, does "dietary and social uses of the community" mean precisely? Or what exactly is meant by "health or his social or economic functioning"? Nevertheless, as a general definition, it serves the purpose more adequately than many others, and I follow it in this book.

Definitional controversies are usually accompanied by word controversies. Any number of words have been proposed in addition to alcoholism and alcoholic to denote the phenomenal process and its individual embodiment. Among the more outlandish ones are alcaddiction, alcodipsion, alcoholites, and alcoholoses. Happily, none of these are in current use.

Practically speaking, most of what I have to say about personality traits of alcoholics is based on talking with and observing persons who come to a doctor or clinic seeking treatment for a problem about drinking. Most of these persons fall within the scope of the

Keller and World Health Organization definition of alcoholism. It is conceivable that those problem drinkers who do not seek out treatment for their difficulty (and they, by the way, are in the majority) have different personality structures from those who do. If this is the case, then this book is to that extent limited in what it says of the personality of the alcoholic. This potential limitation is offset by the fact that some of my observations are based on personal acquaintance with alcoholics who have not sought out treatment. Although my experience is not as wide with these as with publicly identified alcoholics, I hazard the following guess about personality differences between the two: not only is denial of a problem much stronger in the alcoholic who does not seek out treatment, but denial is also easier for him to maintain for three reasons. He is apt to be young, and therefore has not had the problem long; he is apt not to have suffered reality consequences (job or marital difficulties, trouble with the law); or he is apt to be protected by well-to-do parents who clear up his difficulties as fast as they arise.

Except for Chapter 8, this book is about the male alcoholic. This may surprise those who have come to believe that alcoholism is a problem just as common for women as for men. I wish to dispel the idea that undetected hordes of women with alcoholic problems are hidden away in suburbia, protected from disclosure by husbands, children, and a complacent professional community. While their numbers are probably gently increasing, female alcoholics do not yet, and will not in the foreseeable future, present the magnitude of social and health problems that characterize male alcoholics. Some would have it otherwise.

Recently two well-known clinicians commented that the ratio of male to female alcoholics "may now be one-to-one in various urban areas." One of these clinicians even ventured the opinion that "there are now possibly more women than men alcoholics in the country." This increasingly common and widespread supposition is unsupported by the facts. Rather, abundant and relatively clear-cut evidence shows that sex ratios for alcoholism are pretty much what many alcohologists have thought all along, with perhaps a mild increase in alcoholism among women.

How do we determine the number of alcoholics in the country? Who arrives at the figure of five to six million alcoholics in the United States? These statistics are not based on a head count, but represent an estimate computed from a formula developed by the late E. M. Jellinek. The critical variable in this formula is death because of cirrhosis of the liver, a common but indirect result of prolonged excessive drinking. In technical circles, the Jellinek formula is generally accepted as the most dependable device for estimating the number of alcoholics in a community, region, or nation, even though it may be influenced by local variations in the manner of reporting the cause of death, as well as by other factors.

Estimates based on the Jellinek formula reveal a ratio that varies between five and six-and-a-half men to every woman alcoholic. This ratio has remained substantially the same for many years, and there is no indication whatsoever that the number of female alcoholics is dramatically approaching that of men.

Advocates of the view that alcoholism is just, or almost, as much a female as a male problem point first to the decreasing ratio of men to women seeking aid and second to the fact that alcoholic women remain "hidden" from public view. As to the first, there is no question that sex ratios in treatment centers are shifting, but not drastically. In facilities that accept women the ratio is now three or four men to one woman. No one questions that the excessively drinking woman is less publicly visible than her male counterpart and so is apt to be more "hidden." But one can question the use of this idea to support a contention that there are four to five million more alcoholic women in this country than the already estimated three-quarters of a million, and further that these supposed millions of women alcoholics are effectively hidden from view because they are at home. The view implies that women don't have the complications of alcoholism that men do, or that these complications never come to light, or that there is a conspiracy of silence between friendly family doctors (do they still exist?), husbands, and relatives. Listening to the supporters of the one-to-one thesis, one conjures up an image of the husband of the alcoholic woman as the most patient, forbearing, understanding, and masochistic man in the world, whose only interest is to deny his wife's problem or to keep it in the family.

All in all, there is little evidence that alcoholism is a problem of equal, or even close to equal, magnitude for women as for men. I write of the personality of men in this book partly because alcoholism is an illness of men, but partly, too, because much of my experience and most of what has been written about alcoholics pertains to men rather than women. I include a separate chapter on women because my knowledge about them suggests that their personality organization differs from that of men, and while alcoholism is proportionally a man's disease, the actual number of alcoholic women is far from small.

I trust that this somewhat lengthy introductory statement serves a useful purpose in setting the stage for what follows about the alcoholic personality, in showing the limitation of what I say about it, and in a more general vein setting a tone of flexibility for looking at personality factors among alcoholics. In the succeeding six chapters I will discuss in detail six facets of personality commonly observed or reported in alcoholics. The last four chapters will focus respectively on what we know about personality factors among women problem drinkers, on some of the reasons we respond to the alcoholic in the way that we sometimes do, on the therapies now used to treat alcoholics, and, finally, on recent trends toward preventing alcoholism.

2

DEPENDENCY AND MASCULINITY

MAN IS A dependent animal. From birth to puberty, he is biologically dependent on others for food, clothing, and shelter. The relation between biological dependence and psychological dependence—wishes to be cared for, loved, nurtured, to trust in others—has never been adequately explained, yet it is reasonable to assume that psychological dependence finds its genesis in a biological substrate. Psychological dependence begins almost with birth. Given the basic desiderata of physical care, food, clothing, shelter, and medical supervision, infants will nevertheless literally wither away if these are unaccompanied by the presence of a warm, nurturing person. Studies that show this in institutionalized infants suggest the very early beginnings of dependence as a mental phenomenon. Laboratory studies of infant monkeys raised in isolation from their mothers indicate that body contact and warmth are necessary prerequisites to normal development. Schaller's observations of gorillas in their natural state suggest that psychological dependence occurs at the nonhuman primate level. Young gorillas maintain close physical relationships with their mothers long after any biological need to do so. The ubiquitous necessity of dependence in man and some other animals, as well as its early origins at least shortly after birth, if not in the prenatal state, indicates its importance in subsequent development into adolescence, adulthood, and indeed through the life cycle.

13

Psychological dependence in Western society is complicated by the fact that our social values sanction open expression of dependent behavior among men only in special circumstances: in infancy and childhood, in illness, and, reluctantly, in old age. Consequently, man in Western society has had to develop ways of satisfying dependent needs without seeming to be dependent or, alternatively, to force underground wishes to be dependent, to behave as if they didn't exist. The young boy learns this quickly as he is growing up and responds accordingly. Our society affords him little opportunity to experiment with dependency needs and ways of satisfying them that are consonant with any given level of development. The capacity to develop and maintain gratifying dependent relationships is stunted at a very young age. There is little chance for a boy's dependency to grow. Consequently, the tone, the early flavor of dependency needs remains throughout life, pushed underground or repressed from conscious awareness under the pressure of the child's quick perception of society's disfavor toward dependent behavior. Should needs be intense, as they often are, or should they obtrude into behavior in later life, their dominant tone, being derived from infancy and early childhood, is likely to be highly inconsistent with what we value as adult or mature behavior. In such instances, society labels the individual as mentally ill or deviant.

Dependency, and difficulties with it, has been noted by many observers to play a crucial role in the personality of alcoholics. As with any abstraction, dependency has been used with varying connotations to refer to many different things. Dependency has, for instance, been implicated as the primary psychological cause of alcoholism, used to denote the alcoholic's dependence on alcohol, and used to describe him after many years of alcoholism. Sometimes it is viewed as a hypothetical entity, not directly observable, but nevertheless exerting profound influence on the behavior of the individual alcoholic; at other times, it is seen as a concrete behavior that can be directly measured. The former view predicts specific behaviors poorly and too readily gives rise to after-the-fact interpretations; the latter view, on the other hand, oversimplifies the complexity of the alcoholic's psychological make-up. A man may have a great problem with dependent needs and yet not be dependent in his actions. Other writers have subdivided dependency to include lack of dominance in relation to others, financial dependence on others, and descriptions by wives as to the alcoholic's dependency on them. Yet others have used terms other than dependency, such as, orality, passivity, and the need to be loved, that might well be thought of as components of dependency.

I view dependency both as an underlying-need state and as a directly observable behavior that is not in itself a central factor in alcoholism. While dependency as a need state is closely related to dependency as an observable behavior, it is best thought of as an idea, a mental construction, not generally amenable to direct observation. Dependent needs are nearly always of central importance in the alcoholic's personality make-up, but this does not mean, as I have indicated above, that openly dependent behavior is always part of the alcoholic's repertoire of actions. Failure to distinguish between dependency as a motivational state and as a series of measurable actions has caused considerable confusion in professional writings on dependency among alcoholics. Edith Lisansky and the McCords have cogently portrayed the dependency conflict that I assume occurs in most alcoholics. Both authors have, however, stated that alcoholism becomes apparent when the alcoholic, as Lisansky puts it, surrenders to his dependency needs and becomes overtly dependent. Neither clinical experience nor research studies support this conclusion. Many, many alcoholics are not in the least dependent in their surface behavior. *The crucial factor is the way in which the alcoholic solves the conflict over dependent wishes.* At least three solutions can occur, each resulting in a different set of observable behaviors in the alcoholic.

15

One kind of alcoholic relies openly on others, seeking their care and solicitude; we may infer that he has strong dependent needs for which he seeks direct gratification. Alcoholics in this group expect and actively try to get others and the environment to meet their needs, and take initiative only in the service of satisfying dependent wishes, a tendency sometimes referred to as passive mastery. Other than this, they do not take the initiative, do little on their own, and function most adequately when guided firmly and closely. Examination of their life histories reveals two major avenues which led to their present psychological resting place. Some have taken a direct route: the need to be taken care of has always been strong and openly expressed. They have shown little evidence of strivings for independence, even in adolescence, and have usually remained close to the hearth. As adults, they often remain at home in a childlike relationship to parents or to an older brother or sister. Because of the romantic aura of individualism that surrounds the hobo in our society, it may sound initially paradoxical to hear that drifters and wanderers often fall into this group. Alcoholic drifters are usually openly dependent, and a look back into their early life shows that leaving home was often not a matter of choice but a necessity, due to dissolution of the family, rejection, or some other circumstance. These men in their drifting pattern tend to recapitulate the dependent relationships of childhood by developing an attachment to a dominant man or woman who protects and cares for them. The more indirect path closely meets Lisansky's surrender-to-dependency model mentioned above. Men who have taken this route have shown, in the past, strenuous attempts to achieve independent masculine status. As adult requirements for responsibility and independent action increase with age, on the job, in marriage, and in rearing their own children, these men respond with anxiety and tension. Strong and unrelenting dependent wishes remain ungratified. In this situation a surrender of dependency can occur, the man turning increasingly to alcohol and relinquishing adult responsibilities.

16

DEPENDENCY AND MASCULINITY

An instance of the openly dependent alcoholic is a man in his mid-forties who sought help for an alcohol problem. Raised in a well-to-do family by well-meaning parents he was surrounded during childhood and adolescence by a surfeit of material things; his parents were cool emotionally and only able to express their love through gifts and money, rather than warmth and affection. Uncertain of his parents' love but smothered by their largesse, he grew to extort affection from others and to expect all his needs to be met automatically. An intelligent boy, he did well in early school years, but began having some difficulty as schoolwork became more demanding in high school. In his mid-teens, he began to drink at parties and other social occasions where alcohol was available. In college, he did increasingly poorly and finally flunked out in his junior year, failing courses because he didn't attend classes or do the required reading. Socially charming and with good connections, he got into the brokerage business, but went from company to company because he failed to maintain existing accounts, let alone attract new ones. In the meantime, he had married and had two children. From high school on, he drank heavily, but his parents and others considered this as nothing more than youthful high spirits. Maintained occupationally for years through family connections and financially by his wife's small inheritance, he gradually drank more and more, so that alcohol became a major part of his life. Unfailingly easygoing, never nasty or aggressive while drinking, he was a "pleasant drunk," often quietly humorous or solemnly earnest. He took for granted that his wife, parents, and friends would take care of him, and repeatedly re-created the circumstances which made it necessary that they do so. He sought help when he finally ran out of firms that would hire him and his wife threatened to withdraw her support unless he saw someone about his alcohol problem.

A second group includes alcoholics at the opposite pole to those described above. Relationships involving open expression of dependent behavior are studiously avoided. These men see themselves

17

as capable of taking care of themselves, usually deny any problem with alcohol, and pride themselves on acts of physical prowess and masculine achievement. The statement "He can drink like a man" is among their highest forms of praise. They do seek to gratify dependent needs, but indirectly and covertly. The fellowship of the tavern, the sometimes maudlin avowals of friendship combined with superficial relations to others, and dependency on alcohol itself attest to this. This alcoholic has intense dependent needs, the direct satisfaction of which is unacceptable and frightening. The basic conflict is that directly dependent behavior makes him look like a little boy, like a "sissy"; he fears that expressed dependency will dramatically alter his tenuous image of himself to destroy his identity as a man. Alcoholics in this group may be termed counterdependent in order to distinguish them from persons who are independent and yet show that they can form close attachments to others that involve openly dependent behavior. Counterdependence is highly defensive, easily challenged and threatened; independence is flexible, modulated with dependency, and not easily challenged.

The counterdependent alcoholic does not fit the surrender-to-dependency model at all, for in terms of that conception he would still be prealcoholic. Yet alcoholics may be counterdependent regardless of age and how many years they have been drinking alcoholically. Counterdependent, masculine activities have been an integral and probably essential aspect of their lives from early childhood on through adulthood. Leadership qualities, athletic prowess, occupational attainments, are often present; so are fighting, daring but dangerous exploits, often with cars, and on occasion criminal activity. These men often have many friends and acquaintances, yet infrequently show close ties involving open dependent behavior to anyone. They are unable to tolerate periods of inactivity or enjoy quietude. Conflict over dependency has been solved at an early age by submerging from awareness wishes to be

18

dependent and by developing ways of acting that are approved by society as being independent and masculine (or at least as being not dependent) while simultaneously gratifying dependency in ways hidden from themselves and hopefully from others. As long as the pattern can be maintained they see no reason to be other than they are.

An illustration of counterdependency is found in the case of a successful sales manager who was threatened with loss of his job unless he sought help for an alcohol problem that was severely affecting his work and the company that employed him. His father, a successful businessman, had early insisted that his sons be self-reliant and resourceful: all childhood indications of "weakness," softness, tears and so on were subjects for paternal censure. He also had an uncle, alcoholic black sheep of the family, but much-beloved by his nephew; the uncle seemed a free spirit, appearing sporadically and unannounced, in marked contrast to the severe and predictable father.

As the boy grew up, his competitive energies were marked, and he desired to excel all in whatever he attempted; in team sports he was poor not for lack of ability, but because he found it difficult to subordinate himself to a team effort. A hard drinker from his late teens on, he prided himself that his friends could not outdrink him and that he always remained in command of his actions and faculties. When he left school, he went into sales, and through a combination of desire to achieve, intelligence, and hale heartiness he did exceptionally well. Drinking became more frequent at lunch, and into the afternoon, but had little noticeable effect on his work. As years passed, he became sales manager of a national firm, which entailed overseeing the operations of regional offices and contacts with executives in other companies with which his firm transacted business. Drinking on business trips and at conventions continued but with one significant change: when drinking, he began to tell off top-level executives of other companies. When a major account was lost as a result, he was confronted with his behavior. He denied that alcohol was in any way responsible and managed to justify his actions. But other similar episodes followed. Confronted again, he denied any difficulty with alcohol. Finally given an either-or ultimatum, he sought treatment.

In addition to openly dependent and counterdependent alcoholics are those who fall midway between the extremes. These men fluctuate, according to circumstance and current life situation, between denying and displaying dependent needs. Behavior of alcoholics in this group can be confusing and annoying to those around them because it is apparently contradictory and even "willfully" changeable. On one occasion, the alcoholic may go out of his way to lean on others, seeking out their attention or acting only upon their advice or with their consent, while the next time he denies that he requested anything, protests that he is capable of handling his own affairs without turning to others, and criticizes others for unwanted free advice.

Men in this group have failed to achieve a lasting resolution of their dependency conflict, and in this failure is the promise of future growth. They practice a number of temporary, expedient, and more or less fleeting solutions. Apparently not so frightened of dependent wishes that they deny them completely, they show relatively little tendency to regress to a state of unremitting dependent behavior, perhaps because they fear the full expression of dependency in action. Still in the turmoil conflict, men in this group experience conscious pain and anxiety more often than men in either of the other groups. Dependent and counterdependent alcoholics have solved the conflict, one by regressing to dependency, the other by denying its existence. Men in this last group vary their behavior with respect to dependent needs, which implies flexibility and lack of rigidity that can augur well for their future.

Typical of this third betwixt-and-between group is a man in his early thirties, an effective organizer of health services in underdeveloped foreign communities, whose abilities are much in demand, despite a known drinking problem and a related failure to apply his talents consistently. His occupation fits his personal inclinations closely. His jobs in the field are anywhere from six months to two years in duration, and he works and drinks very hard. He is known as a lone operator and shows remarkable success when running his own show with his bosses in the background, preferably thousands of miles away. As a job nears completion, he drinks more and more, but it seems with little effect on his work. When he returns to this country, he does little work other than short-term consultation, continues to drink heavily with noticeable effect on his appearance and general behavior, and forms transient, but close, relationships with women on whom he depends for his meals and a place to live. From time to time, he will control his drinking and start to make plans for another job abroad, but after a few days of enthusiastic initiative these usually fall by the wayside. When he is threatened by complete reliance on others, when he has no more money and has run out of women friends, he returns to his parents and soon obtains a position that takes him out of the country. Whether working or not, he finds life painful and unsatisfying: when working, he is constantly fearful about whether he is doing well; when not, he scourges himself for not doing anything, for letting himself go, and constantly promises himself that he is going to take action about his future.

So here we have three methods alcoholics use to deal with conflict over dependency needs. Each resolution has its own pattern of behavior. What is the relative frequency among alcoholics of each of these behavioral patterns? One study shows that in a group of alcoholics whose behavior on one occasion was examined, 60 percent fitted the openly dependent pattern and 40 percent the counterdependent type. The findings of this investigation do not tell us the frequency of alcoholics falling into the group which wavers between dependent and counterdependent behavior. The way to determine this would be to study a group of alcoholics over a longer period of time, so that one would have repeated observations of their behavior. Irrespective of the relative frequencies of each type of alcoholic, how can a descriptive acquaintance with each aid caretakers who work with alcoholics?

The openly dependent alcoholic can be a source of pleasure or of frustration, according to the context in which the caretaker meets him. When hospitalized, the alcoholic is usually uncomplaining, pleasant, and acquiescent, and the nurse is apt to consider him a "good" patient. He may be overly docile, obsequious, and, if hospitalized for a long time, make little effort to help himself or to shorten the length of his hospital stay. He is "good" because the mere fact of hospitalization is a tremendous source of gratification to him: fed and cared for regularly and efficiently, he is, as a sick person, the socially legitimate recipient of solicitude from those who visit and take care of him. Finally, initiative and independence by patients in a ward setting are often frowned upon and tacitly discouraged by ward staff. The alcoholic's doctor, on the other hand, may feel disappointed or frustrated by lack of medical progress.

Ways of weaning dependent alcoholics from passive satisfactions in ward settings include firm guidance by ward personnel; establishing explicit, but reasonable, goals in achieving medical progress and discharge; avoidance of too-friendly attitudes by ward personnel. Favoritism is not recommended, but dependent satisfactions should not be sharply or unkindly curtailed; in general, an impersonal, but warm professional attitude combined with explicit placing of limits on gratification of dependency wishes will keep the patient from regression, which hinders medical progress.

In the outpatient clinic, hospital, or office setting, careful delineation of limits is critically important. Implicit limits lead the dependent alcoholic to return again and again for help, advice, or various kinds of material aid to a point where staff members feel sorely abused. The nature of limits of course varies with the structure and requirements of the particular setting. Destitute, homeless alcoholics who come to our hospital emergency service are given bus tickets to a state-supported inpatient facility for alcoholics. We also suggest to them that they return to our alcohol clinic for further treatment when they leave the inpatient setting. We found that dependent alcoholics would come many times for tickets without following through on subsequent treatment plans, our practice of giving bus tickets merely reinforcing the alcoholic's dependency without helping him with his problems related to alcohol. We consequently adopted a policy, which we made clear to each alcoholic, that we would give bus tickets on no more than three occasions unless the patient followed up on our recommendations for care after he left the inpatient facility.

In treatment, we discourage the formation of highly dependent attachments to a particular psychiatrist or social worker, unless the patient will obviously benefit from such a relation. Rather, we encourage treatment modalities, for example, group therapy, where the development of dependent relationships is less likely to occur. Sometimes a dependent alcoholic switches his dependence from alcohol to another substance or activity less deleterious to health and welfare. When this occurs, we encourage it. Recently I heard of a man, well on his way toward becoming an alcoholic, who gave up self-destructive drinking after he began to smoke "pot." He claims that pot serves the psychological purposes of alcohol by making him less fearful and freeing him to do his work (he is an artist), with the advantage that he had no hangovers, blackouts, or attacks of guilt about what he did while drinking.

Treatment of the dependent alcoholic does not usually involve insight methods of psychotherapy but the execution of a plan of management that recognizes his manner of handling and expressing underlying dependent needs. We utilize his proclivity to form dependent attachments to the extent that it keeps him in treatment.

Further encouragement is unwise because the patient may stay on dead center, without progressing, or leave treatment when his demands become so exigent that they cannot be fulfilled or when he begins to fear the intensity of his dependent attachment. One young man frequently came an hour or more before the time for his appointment with his therapist and afterwards often stayed several hours chatting with clinic personnel or just hanging around. Every once in a while he would skip an appointment without explanation or call his therapist and request a different appointment time. He was trying to impose, however weakly, some control over his dependency, for his attachment to the clinic periodically frightened him.

In some areas the dependent alcoholic poses particular problems, as in vocational guidance, personnel selection, and placement. Many dependent alcoholics vacillate with respect to seeking employment, and the vocational counselor may find them difficult clients. When the alcoholic sees work as potentially depriving him of dependent satisfaction, he finds himself the object of the epithets "lazy" and "shiftless." He may be seen as unwilling to do for himself. At the same time, openly dependent men, whether alcoholic or not, tend to do well in military service. All material wants are automatically supplied; clear-cut sets of rules and limits obtain; the organization of authority relations is spelled out in detail; and demands for independence and initiative are minimal. These elements of life in the armed forces may recapitulate the dependency-gratifying situation of infancy and early childhood, with the Army or Navy symbolizing a strict, but giving, mother. Nor should we forget that soldiers and sailors are unambiguously labeled as men in a man's world. How can this knowledge help the civilian guidance worker who is trying to solve an occupational problem with a dependent alcoholic client?

Positions offered the alcoholic must contain built-in satisfactions of dependent needs; conversely, they must not make intensive demands for work or activity rewarded only for its own sake. Prior to offering jobs to an alcoholic client, the counselor must establish a warm and trusting relation with him; at first he must be available to the alcoholic on demand. This gratifies the alcoholic's needs, placing him in a more highly motivated state. The counselor must also work within the limits of his client's skills. Starting the dependent alcoholic on a new line of occupational endeavor is usually more than he can bear. Jobs approximating the service situation, regardless of the level of skill involved, are highly appropriate, for example, jobs with living-in arrangements, or where meals are provided, or with clear-cut relations to a firm, but benevolent, authority.

Alcoholics who are trying to make a comeback, after having hit bottom by losing friends, family, job, and often physical health, commonly take a job dishwashing or, as it is known among them, pearl-diving. Pearl-diving is hard work, but requires no initiative and makes few demands; much is overlooked because of a perennial shortage of dishwashers, and meals are always provided. The upper-middle-class man starting out again may, instead of pearl-diving, seek a job in retail sales in a department store, preferably one that caters to persons from his own background. Here the pace is leisurely and civilized; one's future does not depend on the number of sales one makes, and pushy, assertive salesmanship is hardly *de rigueur*. Like pearl-diving, it is either a haven or an undemanding starting point from which to return to former levels of function. In either case it appeals to the dependent alcoholic.

Dependent alcoholics who have been satisfactorily employed in an organization for many years often suffer a flare-up of their condition when promoted to a job that entails fewer dependent gratifications. Personnel officers who are aware of the relation of personality factors to job performance may often prevent such occurrences by careful review of specific recommendations for promotion. Rehabilitative efforts with dependent alcoholics, especially those in their thirties or forties who have shown few previous independent efforts, should focus on goals which constructively utilize the individual's needs to be in a dependent situation. People can be dependent in many ways, yet lead lives gratifying to themselves and others, and useful to society. A major difficulty here is that dependent behavior is so often frowned upon and castigated in our society.

The counterdependent, like the dependent, alcoholic is not easy to work with. By the very nature of his desire to avoid dependent relations, he is actually less often seen by members of helping professions than the dependent alcoholic. He usually comes to our attention through external situations that impel him to us or in ways not obviously related to his drinking problem. In the first instance, he comes to a caretaking setting as a condition of continuing to live with his wife and children, or of continuing employment, or of probation, or because he is brought by the police. Common to all is an element of coercion, which places the caretaker in the unenviable position of facing a client railroaded into a treatment setting which he would never have dreamed of coming to of his own accord. In the second instance, he comes to us with a problem seemingly unrelated to alcoholism, such as a broken leg or pneumonia. During treatment for the specific problem, difficulty with drinking is observed and a specialist called. As in the first situation, the alcoholic sees his problem as the broken limb or the pneumonia and has little interest in discussing his problem with alcohol.

The nurse often finds the counterdependent alcoholic to be a problem. Frequently querulous, he defies routines that his physician has ordered the nurse to carry out and is overly eager to leave the hospital. He is edgy and irritable because he finds himself in the very situation he has struggled all his life to avoid. The dependency implicit in being ill and hospitalized is frightening, and he tries to reinstate counterdependent defenses, sometimes in panicked ways, much to the concern and often dismay of the nursing staff. The nurse who understands him and acts accordingly finds that things go smoothly, and frequently the patient has a salutary effect on the entire ward. Indicating to the patient, for example, that following ward routines and the doctor's advice is not easy, but requires self-discipline, often appeals to the alcoholic's counterdependent defense. Pointing out that other patients find it difficult to live in a ward environment enhances this appeal, especially when the nurse turns to the counterdependent alcoholic for help and suggestions as to how to deal with other patients. When this approach is effective, the alcoholic often becomes a leader among the patients and a focal point of patient morale. The important issue here is that the alcoholic, assuming independence and responsibility, simultaneously gratifies dependent wishes by helping to care for others, but does it in a counterdependent guise. There are two major dangers: the nurse must be careful that the alcoholic does not presume to take over the nursing role completely, and she must take care that the alcoholic does not attempt to organize patients in ways which run counter to the goals of the ward.

On occasion, a counterdependent alcoholic may challenge the expertness of a nurse or physician. This usually involves questioning prescriptions for care. The alcoholic asks why he has to take this pill or that food, or why he has to stay in bed, and so on, and he prescribes for himself, stating with certainty what he should and should not be doing in the interests of his medical recovery. If the medic becomes angry, a cycle of mutual hostility ensues, usually ending in a situation ultimately harmful to the patient's physical condition and sorely frustrating to nurse and doctor. The true nature of this battle has little to do with medication or ward care, but with whether it is patient or caretaker who is in control. Doctors and nurses who are aware of this issue easily nip it in the bud, before it grows to a size virtually impossible to handle. They examine importunities of the patient as serious suggestions, taken at face value and without rancor, and with approval of the patient's active interest in his welfare. The patient's proposals for his care are examined rationally, along with proposals of the medical staff. Because the caretaker has more command over his feelings than the patient, he can suppress his anger when the patient is unable to suppress his own; in the long run this momentary minor irritant can prevent a major problem and prove a source of pride and gratification to doctor or nurse.

Counterdependent alcoholics are usually not seen of their own volition at inpatient treatment centers or other caretaking settings. The clergyman, for example, is apt to hear of this kind of alcoholic from a distraught wife or mother who is uncertain where to turn. Although he may never see the alcoholic husband or son, he may be of indirect help through counseling or other aid given to the relative. If the clergyman does see the alcoholic, it is apt to be a one-time contact in which the problem drinker repents and renounces his drinking so as to avoid further involvement, or in which he denies a problem, claiming that it is the relative who has the problem by relating his own grievances against the wife or mother. In such situations, what paths does the minister or priest have open to him? First, the pastoral counselor does not take sides with relative or patient, and he attempts to avoid moralizing judgments. Whenever possible and feasible, he sees both parties together in order to avoid taking sides; this permits husband and wife to confront each other with their grievances in a setting that does not allow either person to get out of control. Such meetings often have an immediate ameliorative effect on acute family crises. The pastoral counselor has a dual focus: he curbs highly destructive expressions of anger as he seeks to get the couple to come to a mutual decision about how the problem should be handled. He may offer concrete knowledge of professional services available in the community, and he offers his assistance in making an appropriate referral.

Frequently, however, relatives are afraid to tell the alcoholic that they have seen a minister, so that the alcoholic is unaware of what is happening. Very often family crises may be ameliorated when the relative and not the alcoholic is seen professionally. In such instances, when the wife or other relative accepts professional guidance, the pastoral counselor makes a referral to a family service agency, private psychotherapist, or other facility or person as indicated. The often confused and uncertain relative thus has an opportunity to examine her feelings and straighten out her thoughts in order that she may be better able to make the best decision for herself with regard to her problem-drinking spouse.

When the relative does tell the alcoholic that she has been to the minister, he will usually see the clergyman at least once. When the clergyman sees the counterdependent alcoholic parishioner in a one-to-one setting, he must take pains to gratify the individual's counterdependency if he hopes to achieve a satisfactory relationship with him. When the alcoholic states that he is sorry the whole issue came up, because he is dealing quite adequately with his life, the pastoral counselor inquires why he is sorry and how he is handling it. The pastor further takes sympathetic cognizance of the client's grievances against spouse or other family members. Approval of the client's independence, combined with puzzlement over the situation, tends to enlist further involvement from the client. The counselor responds to the alcoholic who flatly denies any problem with drinking by inquiring into the means the client employs to avoid difficulty with drinking, or by asking how he views the situation that has led the relative to seek the clergyman out. Techniques like these often lead to the gradual development of a relationship between alcoholic and counselor that later serves as a bridge to treatment.

Pastoral counseling is but one example of a caretaking situation. The same principles obtain in diverse situations, such as the case of an alcoholic employee referred to a medical industrial service, or an alcoholic sent by a court to a clinic as a condition of avoiding a legal separation from his wife. In all instances, the caretaking problem is to enlist and enhance the alcoholic's tenuous motivation while not abruptly challenging his counterdependent defense.

What of the alcoholic who has no fixed solution to the conflict between wishes to be cared for and fear that he will lose his integrity as an individual if he submits to them? These problem drinkers are more amenable to, and likely to benefit from, treatment than either dependent or counterdependent alcoholics. First, they are in turbulent conflict, the hoped-for alleviation of which prompts them to seek help. The fact that they can tolerate, however painfully, dependent wishes without regressing to a permanent state of dependency implies flexibility of personal expression highly useful in treatment endeavors. This alcoholic, more than either of the others, is the one who comes voluntarily to a caretaker and says, "I have a problem with alcohol that I can't solve. Can you help me?"

This is not to say the dependent-independent alcoholic is a cinch to treat, that there are no problems in motivation, or that he shows a straight-line, smooth progression toward health and away from alcohol. He is, on the contrary, apt to show the more trying features of the dependent as well as the counterdependent alcoholic without any of the redeeming graces of either. When hospitalized, for example, he is apt to be querulous, demanding, and actively seeking dependent satisfactions: he may complain vociferously that the food is terrible, the bed is incorrectly made, or the nurses continually disturb his rest for petty and unnecessary reasons. Neither appeals to his dependent nor counterdependent side have any noticeable effect on him. Little can be done other than to accept the patient's behavior, adopt a kindly professional attitude that does not vary, and avoid the traps the alcoholic unconsciously sets. With a patient of this type one cannot realistically gratify or use constructively either side of the conflict.

30

Some patients in this category are alternators. They do not express both sides of the dependent-independent struggle simultaneously, but alternate between dependent and counterdependent actions. This sometimes makes it difficult to decide whether one is faced with a dependent, a counterdependent, or a dependent-independent alcoholic. Time, however, answers this problem in those cases where the patient's background and past achievements are unknown. When the ward staff assumes that he is overtly dependent, they will proceed in their management on this basis, attempting to utilize the patient's dependent needs therapeutically. If he soon begins to criticize this care and demand a more independent status, one knows he is a dependent-independent alcoholic in whom the appeal to dependency has aroused sufficient anxiety to make him shift to a counterdependent posture. The same pattern occurs with the seemingly counterdependent patient, with a more or less rapid switching to passively dependent behavior.

Two sorts of difficulties arise with alternators which affect the goals of the nursing staff. First, if the nurse persists in treating the patient as if he were a dependent or a counterdependent alcoholic, the patient may assume counterpostures with a vengeance, so that on the dependent side he makes no effort to help himself or on the counterdependent side he continually questions care or devastates patient morale. Second, frequent switching between dependent and counterdependent behaviors is frustrating and disconcerting, to say the least. Awareness of what is going on with the patient can make his behavior easier to tolerate. One does not cater markedly to either side of the conflict but assumes matter-of-factly that ward life is a series of activities, some necessarily involving dependent or independent behavior. An almost extreme consistency of attitude and response on the part of the nursing staff is beneficial for these patients. Inconsistent attitudes between different ward personnel or within a single member of the staff encourage the patient to explore and employ the incon-

31

sistencies in his own struggles. The patient attempts to play one staff member off against another and, by this manipulation, exert a divisive influence on the staff.

Since the problem drinker actively in conflict about dependency wishes poses behavioral problems beyond the other two types of alcoholics, he should be viewed from the start with an eye to helping him to accept referral for psychotherapy. In general, an alcoholic with unresolved dependency wishes responds well to psychotherapy. People who see many alcoholics in their work, but who are professionally unequipped to undertake long-term treatment, often hesitate to bring up the question of treatment for alcoholism with the dependent-independent alcoholic because he seems so contrary. When they do raise the question of treatment, they are often surprised by the immediate positive responses of the seemingly most recalcitrant alcoholics.

A man of great potential drank himself into oblivion almost every day for eight years and, as a consequence, lost his wife, ran through an inheritance, and eventually had to sell his share of his business to his partner. His rather proper parents were appalled at his behavior and worried continually about him, partly out of concern for their own reputation. But they never suggested that he seek help, for they had convinced themselves that then he would turn completely against them. One day the man's legs would not hold him up because he was so poorly nourished, and he collapsed at work. His parents, now thoroughly frightened for his physical welfare, and possibly because they felt that he was so weak that he couldn't conceivably muster serious resistance, approached him with new resolve and told him they were taking him to a special hospital. With a sigh of relief, he acquiesced, and three weeks later, when he was ready to leave the hospital, his father suggested that he see a psychiatrist. The son not only agreed to this, but entered psychotherapy eagerly. His family was amazed.

Alcoholics often consider the possibility of treatment but are afraid to take the first step. When a professional person broaches the subject to them, it frequently has the effect of being just the impetus the alcoholic needs to enter into therapy. Sometimes the alcoholic is afraid to seek treatment himself because it is somehow a public acknowledgment of his alcoholism, about which he is guilty and ashamed. At other times he is unwilling to take an independent step for which he must assume sole responsibility, as if the step were too far removed from his dependency needs. At yet other times he sees entering therapy on his own as a giving in to dependency, as permitting himself too great a reliance on others; if someone else suggests treatment, it is not his decision, but a choice instigated by another person. So he has an escape hatch if he needs one. If he enters and continues psychotherapy, he soon learns that decisions he makes are his own and that it is satisfying to accept responsibility for his own actions.

In summary, no one is certain that there is one personality trait that serves as the central organizing factor among most alcoholics. However, one observer after another has implicated conflict over dependency wishes in one form or another. Details of formulations vary and language differs, but dependency and inner struggles with it form the background of much of what has been said about the alcoholic.

I have tried to show that the personality of the alcoholic revolves about three compromises developed to cope with conflict over wishes to be dependent and the complementary fear that direct expression of dependent wishes will result in loss of self-identity, of masculinity. The choice of compromises is influenced by society's negative attitude toward open avowals of dependency in men and by society's tendency to equate independence and masculinity. Two extreme compromises are repression of independency on the one hand and repression of dependency on the other; both tend to bury the conflict. Problem drinkers in either of these extreme categories have chosen an unbending mode of conflict resolution, and while the anxiety and pain they feel may be relatively low, they have little freedom to choose how they will live. By and large, the caretaking community must settle for the achievement of limited treatment goals with men in these groups. A third compromise is shown by men who have not made a rigid compromise and who still actively cope both with demands to be dependent and with strivings for independence. Men in this group have a higher chance of benefiting from psychological methods of treatment than those in either extreme group. In succeeding chapters I will examine other personality traits as flowing from each of the resolutions of dependency conflict.

3

ANGER AND DEPRESSION

MAN IS AN aggressive as well as a dependent animal. Whether aggressive drives, like dependent needs, are rooted in our biological heritage is unclear. Some, like Freud, have postulated, however uneasily, that aggressive energies proceed from our constitutional make-up, are among the physical givens of our existence. Others have seen aggression as a response to frustration or as a reaction to danger. The important facts for us are that aggressive impulses and actions are ubiquitous in man and make their appearance early in life, as anyone who has seen the reaction of an infant to the abrupt removal of the nipple from his mouth can testify. Important for our discussion of the alcoholic's personality make-up is the cultural fact that society does not readily permit physical or emotional displays of aggression. We must not act or feel angry.

The alcoholic is an angry person, whether he shows it or not. The mild-mannered fellow who becomes a raging lion when drunk is proverbial. We also know from intensive psychotherapeutic experience that the angry wishes and aggressive impulses of alcoholics are intense, no matter how they behave. Close inspection reveals that this anger is born of frustration—and its unrelenting persistence is due to frustration that is continual. What is frustrated and why is frustration continual?

Men in our society, and alcoholics in particular, have little opportunity while growing up to become acceptingly familiar with dependent wishes, because society disapproves of explicitly dependent behavior by men. The need to rely on others has little chance to mature, to change with experiences of dependency. The need undergoes no maturing modifications, but continues to carry the insistence for immediate satisfaction, the demand for gratification without limiting conditions, in a word the insatiability that characterizes infancy and early childhood. In an adult world, this need is inevitably frustrated, and the very fact of frustration keeps the need alive. The alcoholic never relinquishes the inner hope and longing for unconditional love. He searches quixotically for something man cannot have in its entirety. The effects of alcohol may temporarily provide the means to recapture the past, permitting momentary self-transcendence. But repeated rebuffs in the search for passive satisfactions make anger inescapable.

Since this process occurs in the alcoholic's inner experience and is not expressed in his behavior, frustration of dependency and resultant anger occur whether the alcoholic is dependent, counter-dependent, or dependent-independent. Since many mediating steps take place between this internal, unconscious operation and overt action, many alcoholics will not appear to be angry. If we examine ourselves, we see that many times we may feel angry but not show it. This happens when we are aware that our anger makes private but not public sense, or when we are afraid for inner reasons of the results of showing it, or when we are afraid that society will look upon us with disfavor. These are not either-or issues. Rarely are things so neat; rather they intertwine in complex ways that only long-term psychotherapy can untangle. The point is that a person can be angry, and angry all the time, without appearing to be so. Unexpressed angry feelings are typical of Americans. At the same time, we are known as a people to whom incidents of unprovoked violence and sadism are not uncommon, as may be seen in the recent mass slaying of student nurses in

Chicago or in the Whitman shootings on the University of Texas campus. What values create this paradox? All societies teach man, from early infancy on, to channel aggression into paths which are socially useful rather than destructive. In our own society this universal tendency is ambivalently repressive: we scotch almost all direct expressions of anger, while encouraging our children to be "aggressive," that is to say, to be driving and assertive, to take initiative, and to be competitive, often in ways harmful to others. We teach our young to walk an emotional tightrope, a trick that many young people today are refusing to perform. To learn the subtle distinctions involved is an integral aspect of the socialization process, especially for male children. Learning how to use anger without being angry is complicated and unstable because of the inherent contradiction. Many children learn the lesson poorly and are given as adults to apparently inexplicable displays of petulance and anger, reminiscent of the temper tantrums of infancy and childhood, or they may be physically violent, demonstrating what the child in an adult body can do. Others learn to suppress anger too well, as it were, and grow up virtually unable to express anger except in highly indirect ways; one can estimate the degree of inner rage only by minute cues.

Some years ago I saw a young man who, rather than follow in the footsteps of his successful businessman father, wanted to be a poet; he found the futility of modern-day living with its emphasis on money and competition distasteful. During the first months I saw him I was struck by an absence of angry sentiment: he spoke of his feelings of love, charity, gentleness, and tenderness, regretting that others could not share in these feelings as fully as he. This idyllic but unreal self-portrait gradually underwent a transformation: first he related, with quiet and shame, how he tortured a household pet when a child; then came his jealous envy of his father's success; his need to withdraw from a ruthlessly competitive society gave way to a fear of entering into competition with his father; and, finally, his dammed-up fury toward his father (who had tried to suppress all expression of feeling in his children) burst forth, accompanied by fantasies of brutality and annihilation.

How directly does the alcoholic express his internal rage? Contrary to popular and even professional belief, violent, physically assaultive behavior by alcoholics is vastly overestimated. To be sure, we have all heard of instances of wife-beating and abusive treatment toward children, although the frequency and intensity of such occurrences tend to be melodramatically exaggerated. After all, we are fascinated by violence and like to find it where it doesn't necessarily exist. Similarly, we have all heard about drunken brawls and tavern fracases. Although many caretakers (who may themselves feel considerable hostility toward alcoholics) aver that alcoholics are violent, we rarely hear of a case of as-saultiveness by an alcoholic in the experience of the emergency service of our hospital, and we see hundreds of alcoholics a year in varying stages of inebriety. Actual assault occurs in far less than one percent of our patients.

When does the alcoholic resort to physical violence? Open aggression is most apt to occur with those toward whom the alcoholic feels close and toward whom he frequently turns to gratify dependent needs. Even here the frequency of actual assault is subject to hysterical exaggeration. Under the influence of alcohol, submerged rage may come to the surface against those the alcoholic expects to gratify his inner desires. In my experience, assault under these circumstances occurs only occasionally, and other forms of aggression, such as verbal attacks, sarcasm, and teasing provocation, are more the rule. Barroom brawls or fights usually prove on analysis to be the outcome of a constellation of inner events, to which anger, although always present, often assumes a subsidiary and defensive role. When an individual's masculinity has been impugned, a fist fight is a convincing way of reaffirming a threatened masculine image. Anger shows itself in many ways, some more direct than others. The alcoholic, like the rest of us, is not stranger to the gamut of possibilities, although he tends toward indirection rather than straightforwardness.

How are anger and depression, two states of feelings apparently unconnected with one another, related? We may begin to answer this question by describing depression. A seriously depressed person feels worthless and unattuned to living: he suffers from loss of appetite and is unable to sleep. Preoccupied with thoughts of self-destruction, obsessed by sinfulness to the point that he responds little to those around him, he may attempt to take his own life. Although he feels sad, not angry, the depressed person thinks and acts against himself in precisely the way that he would if he were angry with someone. Depression has been conceived as anger turned inward. Further, in situations where someone else is clearly at fault, the depressed person does not become angry at the other person, but takes all blame upon himself. Unable to express anger toward another, he turns it against himself, transforming it into depression. Basically, the depressed person is an angry person. A common observation in psychotherapy is that depression vanishes when the patient airs his anger.

What of less severe episodes or moods of depression, feelings of sadness, blue feelings, feelings of self-disgust, that we all experience at one time or another? Do these bear the same relation to anger as severe, suicidal depression? If we look into ourselves when we are sad or blue, we generally find that we do not like ourselves very much, or that we are critical or sorry about something we have said or done. In other words, during those blue periods we are mad at ourselves. How does this relate to the alcoholic?

Given his fury at the frustration of dependent needs and given society's prohibitions against open expressions of anger, it becomes clear that one of the few outlets for the alcoholic is himself. This is not to say that all alcoholics are severely depressed, although suicide rates are higher for alcoholics than for the general population. Nevertheless, chronic depressed feelings occur regularly in alcoholics. Depression is a painful, unpleasant state of feeling, another thing that the alcoholic must fight against by trying to force it out of awareness or by trying to drown it in alcohol.

I once saw a man in treatment who had witnessed his father's accidental death; my patient was thirteen years old at the time. He portrayed himself as a carefree man-about-town who perhaps drank a bit too much. Actually, he had a serious drinking problem that had begun shortly after his father's death. Alcohol helped him to avoid facing his depressed feelings and his unconscious belief that he had caused his father's accident and, therefore, death. This latter came out indirectly in his dreams and explicitly in remarks he made as he was coming out of anesthesia after an operation.

Alcoholic bouts often begin when the alcoholic senses the imminent upsurge of depressed feelings. Benders, sprees, and bouts are commonplace among alcoholics during the Christmas season. Popular tradition attributes this to the old saw that any excuse is a good one when it comes to drinking. But any alcoholic will tell you that Christmas and New Year's Eve are the worst times of year for him. He drinks not out of jollity or seasonal good cheer, but in the hope that alcohol will provide him with a bulwark against the poignant sadness and sense of loss these holidays, with their emphasis on loving and caring, evoke in him.

Alcoholics may express anger outwardly but, as we have seen, not frequently in the form of assault; or they may turn their anger against the self, so that depression is apparent. What differences do dependent, counterdependent, and dependent-independent alcoholics show in the ways that they handle angry feelings? In general, the dependent alcoholic shows more depression than anger, while the counterdependent alcoholic shows the reverse.

Since anger in the alcoholic is intimately connected with unsatisfied dependent wishes, anger is at a high point when dependency is aroused. Alcoholics frequently express anger by demanding and insisting that dependent needs be satisfied, and often the more one gratifies these demands, the greater they become. The form of the demand is usually phrased in such a way as to give the impression that, whatever the reality limits of a situation, the demand is legitimate and based on the alcoholic's rights as an individual. For example, a patient came to the clinic nearly three hours after the time for his appointment and demanded to see his therapist; when informed that his doctor had left for the day, he became furious, claiming that he was being unfairly treated. Sometimes the demand is one for preferential treatment, as in the case of a man who insisted every two or three weeks that his appointment be shifted to another time because he was a busy man who couldn't possibly keep to a set schedule. Naturally, insistencies like these can evoke feelings of anger in the recipient of the demands. Another form of anger is criticism of others for what they have not done, or what they have not given to the alcoholic. It is fairly typical for me to hear a new patient berate a doctor he has previously seen, telling me how unqualified and irresponsible this practitioner is, going to some lengths to justify his position. One feels put on notice also. When he is not drinking, the alcoholic will complain and gripe to a friend about the way his wife treats him, the focal point of his complaints usually being that she doesn't do such-and-such for him. When he is drinking, his recriminations may be expressed directly and not through a third party. Sometimes his hostility will be thinly veiled by sarcasm or allusively bitter statements. The third-party situation appears to be one feature that makes the bonhomie of the barroom, in that two or more men will express their mutual complaints, which gives them a sense of community of spirit and a feeling that they are together, all injured parties. This, of course, is common not only to alcoholics, but to most of us; but unlike most of us, the alcoholic finds this a constant balm for his feelings of

41

anger and frustration. Some scenes from O'Neill's *The Iceman Cometh* capture this comradeship-in-anger perfectly.

The demandingly angry alcoholic alienates others and provokes anger. It is almost as if he wishes to be rejected. Why he does this when his major goal in life is to be cared for and loved is a paradox worth further examination. He fears the intensity of dependency, seeing in its gratification a devastatingly frightening relinquishment of self. This fear is especially seen among counter-dependent and dependent-independent alcoholics. At more conscious levels, the alcoholic feels unloved and emotionally expendable. The bottle is truly a more constant companion than people. Encouraging others to cast him out becomes a way of reinforcing his image of himself, the image that helps him to justify his drinking to himself.

How can caretakers help the alcoholic to show anger more forthrightly, rather than turning it upon himself? Many of the suggestions and admonitions discussed in the chapter on dependency apply as well to anger and depression. The cardinal principle is to respond to the alcoholic's anger in ways which do not serve to reinforce the hidden aim of being rejected. Again, carefully pointing out reality and delineating limits is particularly important when one is confronted with an importunate dependent alcoholic. But for those interested in reaching and helping the alcoholic this is not sufficient. If we give him merely rules and regulations, the alcoholic will feel that our concern is less for his than for our comfort. Clarification of limits for its own sake has no meaning— it must be done with genuine interest in the alcoholic and his welfare. To expect thanks from him, or even a diminution of demandingness, is to prepare oneself for a disappointment, for the caretaker's delineation of limits and his interest frequently spur the alcoholic on to renewed and more vigorous importunities. The alcoholic's frustrated desire to be rejected combined with our gestures of friendliness and interest are inviting but frightening to him. He tests us with a new demand or by showing us that we have made an error by being nice to him. This makes the caretaker's life difficult; but if he perseveres, sometimes over prolonged periods, he will find that the alcoholic gradually opens up, makes fewer demands, and begins to respect if not like him. More important, the alcoholic begins to respect himself.

When the practitioner, whatever his profession, fails to take these psychological realities into account, he will find that his alcoholic clients fail to respond to him and shortly discontinue contact. Discontinuance of treatment, rehabilitation, and other relationships by alcoholics is too common and has led many professionals to insist that the alcoholic is not treatable because he will not stay in treatment, or that he is not motivated to help himself. These caretakers have apparently not considered the possibility that a change in their own sometimes inflexible, sometimes oversolicitous, counterhostile approaches to alcoholics might result in more clients maintaining contact longer and more beneficially. An investigation at our hospital showed that when we approached them with firm kindness, a respect for their dignity as individuals, and with due appreciation of their inner conflict over dependency, alcoholics formed treatment relations more frequently than experiences reported by others would suggest.

The alcoholic who expresses angry feelings by attempting to enlist the caretaker in a struggle against a spouse, parent, or friend presents another treatment problem. As indicated earlier, the caretaker is wise not to side with the alcoholic. The alcoholic is often extremely convincing and may in fact represent the reality of his situation accurately. Even more seductive is the alcoholic's insinuation that if the caretaker will take sides with him, he will go along with what the caretaker is trying to accomplish. Why should the caretaker not side with the alcoholic? First, the caretaker who takes sides usually finds that he has lost a client. The alcoholic unconsciously knows that he is trying to manipulate the caretaker;

if he succeeds, he feels no respect for and no source of control in the caretaker. Once the alcoholic knows that he can fool the caretaker, he wonders about the help he can expect from someone he can use so easily to forward his self-destructive drives. Secondly, when a caretaker sides with an alcoholic, the alcoholic often uses the caretaker's backing in disputes that arise within the family. This heightens, rather than ameliorates, external conflict. The alcoholic may become a go-between, telling the caretaker what his relative said against the caretaker, and the relative what the caretaker said against the relative.

When the caretaker distinguishes between facts and feelings expressed by his client, he has taken the first step in enlisting the client's motivation, while not taking sides. Next, he responds to feelings not to facts. When an alcoholic says, "Without even talking it over with me, all of a sudden my wife went to a lawyer to get a legal separation and to kick me out of my own home. What do you think of that?" the caretaker does not respond by saying, "I think that's terrible," or even by saying, "Tell me more about it." Both statements lead to a focus on facts, since the first is a direct taking of sides, and the second moves in that direction. Instead, the caretaker reflects the client's feelings by saying, "You were furious," or "You felt let down," or "That must have been frightening," depending on whether anger, hurt, or anxiety is the dominant feeling tone expressed by the client. Remarks like these show the client that he is understood, and understanding is a basis for trust. They also help the client to look deeper into his feelings while bringing the reality situation into clearer focus. The client-caretaker relation is strengthened, and the issue of who is right or wrong is side-stepped.

The openly depressed alcoholic is a somewhat different problem. The caretaker must first determine the severity of the depression. If the alcoholic expresses fear of taking his life, is deeply apathetic, has lost his appetite, and is unable to sleep, he may well be suffering from a severe and dangerous depression. In such cases, a psychiatrist should be sought immediately; if one is not available, the client should be referred to any other physician. Referral of a psychotically depressed person is usually not difficult to make because the alcoholic himself usually recognizes the extent and severity of his disturbance and wants help. It is necessary to inform the patient's relatives of his condition and to enlist their cooperation, since hospitalization is frequently required for a severe depressive episode.

The nonmedical caretaker fortunately does not face this problem often. The client typically is mildly depressed, that is, he feels down in the dumps; life seems to hold little prospect for him; and he is uninterested in what he does. These moods come and go, and usually the caretaker does not focus directly on them until he knows his client well and has been working with him some time. Depression is usually a surface manifestation of conflict, so it must be approached circumspectly lest the client raise his defenses and flee. Sympathetic listening, with an ear out for where and toward whom the client's anger is directed, results in a lessening of a mildly depressed mood after one or two contacts. Attempting to jolly a client out of a depressed state is ineffective and may even deepen his sadness, since it increases resistance because he feels he is faced with one more person who should understand him, but doesn't. When anger underlying depression comes out into the open, the depression generally ceases. Depression is a feeling state best dealt with in a psychotherapeutic setting. Nurses, general physicians, clergymen, guidance personnel, and others who see alcoholics for brief periods can be sympathetic listeners for mildly depressed alcoholics. It is always unwise to agree with the alcoholic in his depressed opinion of himself; such agreement sometimes reflects nothing more than our own hostility, and it maintains depression. The nonpsychiatric practitioner may use his contacts with the alcoholic to make a referral for treatment at a specialized alcoholism clinic.

I have adopted the view that aggression and anger play an important part in the personality of the alcoholic, but are secondary to dependency. Not everyone agrees with me. Some see anger as occupying the position of a central organizing tendency, a position I reserve for dependency. Karl Menninger, for example, described alcoholism as a form of self-destruction based on a need to avoid "a greater self-destruction." Menninger's admirable portrayal of the alcoholic's personality fails to distinguish between two levels of psychological function. Few would question that the alcoholic destroys himself in the sense that he fractures relationships with others, injures himself severely in his job, suffers in his physical health, and deteriorates economically. Here Menninger's term "slow suicide" is descriptively apt. To conclude that the consequence of alcoholism is its major psychological motivating force is, however, a fallacy. Alcoholism is undoubtedly self-destructive, and the alcoholic is the undoubted prey of destructive forces, but neither means that the key to understanding the personality structure of the alcoholic is to be found in aggressive impulses. As I view it, aggression proceeds primarily from the blocking of dependent desires. Aggressive impulses vary in intensity and strength from person to person and, even when strong, are generally subsidiary to conflict over dependent needs. As another observer has put it, Menninger "overlooks the deep striving of the alcoholic to be loved and appreciated by society." The alcoholic drinks not because he wants to kill himself; he drinks to preserve himself and to maintain his integrity. That prolonged excessive drinking ultimately destroys rather than preserves, decomposes rather than maintains integrity, that its effects are opposite to those the drinker seeks through it are among the paradoxes of alcoholism.

4

DENIAL

"ALL ALCOHOLICS deny their problem."
"He cannot be treated until he stops denying."
"Denial is the alcoholic's main defense."
These are the professional shibboleths one hears about alcoholics. Denial as word and concept is employed in ways which obscure rather than clarify our understanding of alcoholics. In its traditional psychiatric meaning, denial refers to an unconscious blotting out of realities, the recognition of which could trigger off anxiety sufficient to overwhelm the integrity of the individual's personality. Over the years, however, the meaning of denial has come to encompass any indication that part of reality does not exist—which is perfectly acceptable, provided one distinguishes between psychological processes that underlie denying remarks and acts. Unfortunately, in everyday work we are often casual and imprecise and fail to make these distinctions. And so the same word, denial, may be used to lump together different psychological happenings, and sometimes we may fail to realize that the happenings are indeed different. The first is a word-error, the second a thinking-error. Neither is in the alcoholic's best interests. Only when we disentangle the usages of denial and order them on a scale from normal to abnormal, can we determine the role denial plays in the alcoholic's personality.

The individual who relies upon denial in its traditional sense is severely disturbed, usually psychotic, and often requires hospitalization. An adolescent, for example, because of several consistent inner insistencies denied that his parents were his. The uncompromising quality of his denial was unmistakeable: for him it was a matter of fact that these people were not his parents. He didn't merely doubt that they were his parents nor did he question, as many people do, his parentage; rather he found the claim of this man and woman to be his father and mother patently absurd. Acting on this inner "fact," which made sense to him, the adolescent behaved in inappropriate and disturbed ways.

In denial in this extreme form, what is denied simply does not exist for the individual. No amount of reason, argument, or demonstration can sway this *idée fixe*. Severe denial is resistant to change and does not fluctuate with circumstances. Denial is also accompanied by an unconscious and irrational fear that to accept the existence of what is denied is to destroy oneself. Further, what is denied is grossly apparent to everyone but the denier and usually has to do with a major aspect of his life. Finally, the consequences of denial permeate and affect one's entire existence. Delusions of being Christ, for instance, or the recipient of communications from other galaxies are based in part on denial. Denial in this extreme and abnormal form is usually called psychotic denial.

Normal, or nonpathological denial, is not blanket, unqualified ignoring of reality; it does not share the categorical qualities of psychotic denial. Unlike psychotic denial, its intensity varies with circumstances, and reason and demonstration can break through it. A person who feels cornered, or under stress, may deny facets of reality which on later reflection he can recognize and accept. Fear of recognizing what is denied is not deeply buried within the person, and he may feel only momentarily or transiently that denial is necessary to self-preservation. What is denied is often relatively trivial and usually has little import for one's core of being. Normal denial does not remake one's style of life, nor does it affect gross behavior.

Denial in everyday life may be seen in the job applicant who says that he is not worried about an upcoming interview with a personnel manager; or the student who at exam time evinces no concern about the outcome of the tests; or the person who in the heat of argument refuses to recognize a fact which at a quieter time he can accept. Instances like these, being part of daily experience, go unnoticed. We casually attribute them to human nature.

Types of denial that fall between normal and psychotic denial are particularly observable in physically disabling afflictions, alcoholism, and what is known as the "phantom limb phenomenon." Common to each is the use of denial to denote, "I do not have a problem; I am not physically disabled; I am not an alcoholic; I have not lost a limb." Denial in these instances is neither psychotic nor normal. Close examination shows that the denying statements are equivocal and not consistently acted upon. Despite awareness that he is disabled, and despite his being told that he will not regain lost function, the physically impaired person continues to hope and believe that in time he will be completely well. The amputee may be convinced that his leg is still there, for he feels sensation and even movement where it was; he also knows that his leg *has been* amputated, and he does not attempt to walk without aid. The alcoholic, where the facts are clear-cut, *will* admit that he has had one or more unfortunate episodes because of excessive drinking, although he will not admit *to others* that alcohol is a vitally necessary part of his existence. In each instance the individual sways back and forth between wish and reality: when the wish dominates, denial is intense; when reality dominates, denial is weak. The tragic struggle between hope and actuality is necessary to the process of adjustment to physical loss, similar in many respects to grieving over the death of a loved one. With the alcoholic this alternation reflects an internal conflict between the wish that he were free of alcohol and the inner knowledge that he is not.

The word *denial,* used to describe an alcoholic's reluctance to admit an alcohol problem or to describe a disabled person's dif-

49

ficulty in recognizing the irreversibility of handicap, lies somewhere between psychotic and normal denial. In an alcoholic, denial is a conscious difficulty in admitting to others that alcohol determines much of his behavior and inner life. It is neither the primitive defensive stance of the psychotic nor the benign garden variety we see in everyday life. Many observers assume denial to be the invariable concomitant of alcoholism. If so, is it an invariant process or does it vary in extent and severity from person to person, or even within a person? Is the "breakdown of denial" necessary to successful treatment of the alcoholic, as many therapists aver? Finally, what are some of the ways that the caretaker may approach the denying alcoholic without alienating him?

Most people find it difficult to admit that their actions are beyond conscious control, and even more difficult to accept that they are unable to exercise decision-making powers in relatively petty matters. To admit that one is in the clutches of something beyond conscious control is an affront to one's sense of dignity, pride, and self-possession. Aversion to admissions of inability to control oneself is aggravated in a society that values self-determination, free will, and individual freedom. We like to think of lack of self-control as a problem of drug addicts and alcoholics, but it is manifest in less exotic and more homely instances in everyday life.

The lengths we will go to to avoid recognition that we are under the control of something seemingly alien to us are amusing. The most obvious example is smoking, which is fast reaching the dubious status of an addiction. Those of us unable to give up smoking rarely admit that we no longer dominate the weed, but that the weed dominates us. Rather than make such an unflattering admission, we engage in a variety of face-saving devices, some more complicated than others. Common maneuvers include such statements as, "It's just a habit," or a flat "There's nothing wrong with smoking." (The question, "What's wrong with smoking?" ceased to be of service a decade ago.) More elaborate maneuvers are practiced by those who keep abreast of the literature relating smoking to cancer and other illnesses in order to develop "reasoned" critical attacks on the conception, methods, and statistics of various studies. One man I know attempted, but failed, to give up smoking. He said he got so irritable when not smoking that it affected family harmony, and he gained so much weight that he feared high blood pressure would result. He now smokes complacently for reasons of health. Nor does smoking exhaust the list of commonplace examples: collecting, golf, bridge, and other avocational pursuits that become minor ruling passions are rarely admitted to be lusts; their continuation becomes rather the basis for an entire series of rationalizations.

Denial of this kind shades from normal to neurotic, but the instances above show that denial is a universal human characteristic, hardly the sole province of alcoholics or other ill persons. The examples also show, by contrast, the extraordinary lengths to which the alcoholic must go if he is to avoid admitting his problem. Consider the energy and ingenuity we expend over trivial addictions, and then imagine the enormous energy required to escape admission that alcohol controls one's functioning. Imagine the anxiety about hidden bottles, the uncertainty over whether Sen-Sen works, the efforts to keep shaking hands from view, the tension over how explanations of public debacles have been received—with his life continually complicated by lack of knowledge of what occurred during periods of "blackout."

It appears, however, that not all alcoholics outwardly deny that their problem with alcohol is beyond control—this, despite what we have repeatedly been told about the generality of denial among alcoholics. In the emergency service of our hospital, which sees nearly 2,000 alcoholics each year, many alcoholics readily admit to an alcoholic problem out of control. Such admissions vary with the ways in which dependent needs are handled, as well as with the length of excessive drinking. The openly dependent alcoholic, especially if the alcohol problem is of long duration, is more apt to admit a problem than either the counterdependent or dependent-independent alcoholic. He does not have to portray himself as independent, masculine, and master of his fate, as do other alcoholics. Further, his active need to get things done for him, and to receive the attentions of others, is best served by admitting his problem. In encounters with those who help alcoholics, he is ready to admit his problem in order to obtain attention.

The dependent alcoholic's admission of his problem need not mean that he is genuinely in search of help for his difficulty. The primary goal is to gratify dependency through attention, and only secondarily to change the alcoholic picture. From a rehabilitative point of view, the dependent alcoholic's admission can mislead caretakers who see the admission as a major step toward recovery.

How does one know when absence of denial portends a sincere wish to change, rather than a bid for attention? A dominant cue resides in the quality with which the admission is proffered. Empty admissions are unsolicited, glib, and may be presented in self-dramatizing terms. The tone may be confessional, as if to say, "I am a bad boy and want to mend my ways." This reminds one of an attention-seeking youngster who is indifferent whether attention is approval or disapproval, so long as it is attention. When the alcoholic presents himself as an alcoholic in need and desirous of changing himself, but without any external inducement or threat and without relating any history of struggle in becoming aware of being alcoholic, it is unlikely that the drive toward change is strong enough to subdue the pleasure of drinking. I have known an alcoholic for a long time who tells me each time I see him about his problems and his resolution to stop drinking, yet he continues to drink. His acceptance and awareness that he is under alcohol's control obtains only at a superficial level and fails to withstand stronger forces within him. He believes that it pleases me to hear of his new resolve, and if I am pleased, then perhaps I will do something nice for him.

The admissions, or confessions, described above are similar to the telling of the alcoholic's "story" in group meetings of Alcoholics Anonymous. Attention received by a speaker from his A.A. audience varies in proportion to the degree to which he can effectively portray the ravages of alcohol on himself and his loved ones. The more self-degrading a portrayal, the greater the sympathy, understanding, and support he receives from the audience. The dependent, nondenying alcoholic gains from telling his story. If the boost to narcissism is great, and reinforced by repeat performances, the internal inducement may be sufficient for him to change his drinking practices.

Denial takes a more severe turn in the counterdependent alcoholic, for it is strong and may persist despite obvious evidence of a problem. Denial by counterdependent alcoholics is more than the aforementioned face-saving maneuvers and gains its impetus from sources other than wishes that a problem with alcohol didn't exist. It is linked to the need to preserve an image of masculinity, independence, and self-sufficiency. The counterdependent alcoholic, his existence predicated on conscious mastery of self and destiny, cannot accept his subjugation to a substance that he knows he could control if he were truly in command of himself. The denying, counterdependent alcoholic, confronted with inescapable evidence that alcohol has caused him trouble, takes pains to justify drinking and its consequences on the grounds of external factors over which he has no control. Sometimes his justifications are ingenious and convincing, but more often they are obvious and shallow. The denying alcoholic seeks company among those who accept and support his scheme of justification, and avoids those who challenge his rationalizations. This is the most pathological form of denial among alcoholics, one most closely approaching psychotic denial. Yet it is unlike psychotic denial because delusions, hallucinations, thought disturbances, and other psychotic signs are absent in the alcoholic (I am speaking of alcoholics who are not psychotic), and because the denying alcoholic can find people who support his denying contentions, whereas thhe psychotically denying person is nearly always perceived as way out.

Discord between an alcoholic and his wife arises when she sees excessive drinking as a threat to family stability and confronts the husband with this knowledge repeatedly, while also challenging his rationalizations as excuses. The husband who is a problem drinker responds to these concerted and repetitive assaults on denial in one of three ways. He counterattacks and gets angry; when successful, the alcoholic so thoroughly cows his wife that she fears to raise the question of drinking with him except at times of extreme crisis, such as job loss, arrest, or an accident. Or he attempts to conceal drinking practices more cleverly than before: he exercises greater ingenuity in hiding the source of supply, drinks alone or in secret more often, or increases drinking away from home. Reliance on either of these techniques further endangers the marriage, isolating husband from wife and eroding mutual trust. The alcoholic increasingly seeks out groups where heavy drinking is sanctioned or at least condoned. Even this becomes awkward or impossible to do if he drinks more than others, or if episodes of vomiting, blackouts, inexplicable anger, or other unacceptable behavior occur and reoccur. Thirdly, his wife's confrontations may be taken seriously, and the husband may examine his behavior in a new light. I know of instances where drinking problems of serious proportions were stopped when the individual came to realize and accept what he was doing. Caretakers don't see examples of this in the way of business. It may be an underestimated occurrence.

The confirmed alcoholic, rejected by family and society, drinks alone or with other alcoholics in places removed from the sanctions of middle-class society. Such a setting has been sensitively portrayed by Eugene O'Neill in the barroom that serves as the locale for the action in his play, *The Iceman Cometh*. Here the dreams of the alcoholic characters are preserved intact, their wished-for fulfillment viewed as a matter of imminent realization, with each character supporting the dreams of the others. Each is always on the edge of departing to realize himself and his ambitions, and always at the last moment something occurs to prevent his leaving. At the same time, each actor knows deep within himself that his dreams are only dreams that will remain unfulfilled. But he must go on deluding himself, and when his recognition of delusion is at a peak, he turns to the mystery of alcohol.

The dependent-independent alcoholic is like the counterdependent alcoholic in his denial, with a critical difference: he permits himself to be aware that he fools himself. Awareness is heightened when gratification, rather than denial of his dependent needs, is foremost in his mind. The more he is aware of his problem, the greater is his internal pain, and the more apt he is to seek to reduce the state of tension. Tension is often relieved by recourse to alcohol, but at these times he is more ready than usual to seek help. He, unlike the counterdependent alcoholic, is able to relinquish denial, especially if he does not thereby consciously destroy his need to be counterdependent. If he has a reason that does not challenge independence and self-determination, he can give up denial.

Many who have written about the treatment of alcoholics hold that breakdown of denial is the first major step in successful treatment. This is one of those statements of "universals" that abound in the literature on alcoholism and reflect a need of many professionals to rely on faith and dogmatic assertions as a substitute for knowledge about a disorder that has thus far defied understanding and control. More acceptable, but less inclusive, is the view that the attainment of some treatment goals requires that denial be minimal. However, some treatment objectives can be reached independently of the degree and kind of denial employed by the alcoholic. The goals we set in treatment have a direct bearing on the type of therapeutic approach we choose. If we aim with one patient toward a basic transformation of his personality structure, an attempt to resolve the conflict between dependency wishes and counterwishes, it will be necessary for the patient to be completely aware that alcohol has a grip on him that he is unable to break by conscious efforts. If, on the other hand, our goals are more limited and specific, for example, keeping a patient out of jail, reducing marital tension, or helping a patient to support himself, the breakdown of denial is often irrelevant to the purposes and practices of treatment. Many alcoholics who persist in denying an out-of-control problem with alcohol have nevertheless reduced their alcoholic episodes to a point where they function adequately in family, job, and social relations. Granting dependency wishes in therapeutic encounters with a person who comes to be trusted and respected is usually the basis for such changes, without the alcoholic having to admit and genuinely accept his problem with alcohol.

Limited-goal treatment is frequently the treatment of choice for dependent and counterdependent alcoholics, and more ambitious goals are ordinarily doomed to failure. It is the dependent-independent alcoholic who is most suited for intensive psychotherapy wherein he can come to understand himself in depth and accept alcohol as an important substance, to be used but not abused. And this patient must give up denial early in treatment.

Denial is always weakened when dependent supplies are in immediate danger of abrupt withdrawal; then denial is replaced by open admission of a problem, combined with willingness to seek out help. This emergency maneuver reinstates a previous balance of forces and occurs regardless of whether the alcoholic is dependent, counterdependent, or dependent-independent. Though breakthrough of denial during crisis is usually expedient, motivation to change is relatively great, and it is wise to attempt to capitalize on this. The alcoholic is willing to follow his wife's suggestion, whether it is to stop drinking, go to a minister or priest, see the family physician, or seek out a clinic for alcoholics. The latter, of course, is usually the best choice, since here the alcoholic will meet professionals adept at enhancing motivation.

Some alcoholics react to dependency crises with genuine internal reorganization, although this is little spoken of in the literature. I have known several men in whom marked changes took place after crisis. I recall one man whose excessive drinking was threatening his livelihood and causing severe disruption of family life. Faced with an unequivocal choice between changing his drinking habits or losing his family, he gave up drinking entirely for a period of several years. He now drinks frequently on social occasions and weekends, but never to a point where it affects his functioning.

Instances like this may occur less rarely than has been supposed. What occurred in this man is not psychologically clear, but it appears to share processes in common with other sudden shifts in personality, such as religious conversions or neuroses that follow upon a sudden and particularly shocking happening. Reactions to sudden, unexpected events can reorganize lives and result in heightened ego function, as well as lead to pathological reactions. Little is known about the internal events and factors that might enable us to predict which way an individual will turn in crisis. Nor do we know if "spontaneous" recoveries occur frequently: they are not often seen in caretaking settings.

Caretakers usually see alcoholics whose breakthrough of denial is transitory, ceasing abruptly when the dependency crisis is past. This phenomenon is one reason for the high rate of patients dropping out of treatment before really getting started. The alcoholic keeps his fingers crossed when he admits his problem, in order to maintain his source of dependent satisfactions. Once the crisis is past, he can relax and go back to his denying ways.

The nurse, social worker, or general physician who wants to

help alcoholics obtain specialized treatment may keep two things in mind. First, the alcoholic doesn't have to stop denying before an appropriate referral to a facility for alcoholics can be made; by appropriate I mean a referral which will probably result in the patient entering and staying in treatment. Second, alcoholics who readily admit their alcoholism should not be immediately referred for treatment.

It is naturally tempting to take immediate advantage of an alcoholic's ready admission that he is an alcoholic seeking help by making a hasty referral to an alcohol clinic. As we have seen, however, facile admissions of problems are often a smoke screen covering desires to receive attention. An immediate referral may result in an abortive therapeutic situation when the patient discovers that the primary purpose of treatment is not necessarily to dispense attention. Such occurrences are frequent and represent an inefficient use of the time of specialized treatment personnel. Rather than a quick referral, the wiser course may be to confer with the patient several times in order to discover more precisely what he is seeking. If it turns out to be attention, a referral is perhaps not the best course of action. One way of discovering the patient's intent is to request that he relinquish something, perhaps cut down on his drinking. His ability to follow through on such a suggestion is a clear-cut indication that he is serious about wanting to help himself. With the ready admitter, a referral to A.A. usually is the most propitious step to take, for A.A. serves a particular and probably beneficial purpose for the dependent alcoholic who only too easily discusses his problem. Another function of meeting with the dependent nondenier on more than one occasion before deciding to refer him to a clinic is simply to see whether he will keep his appointments with you. Often enough he will not, because what he seeks cannot be given by you in the ways that are vital to him.

The nurse frequently encounters patients whose general health is affected by a problem with alcohol. Denial of the problem doesn't mean that the nurse can't help him with it. In contacts with the patient she can assess precisely the areas of the patient's life that are affected by his alcoholic problem; where possible, she can enlist the aid of family members. The aim here is to pinpoint areas in the patient's life which he himself considers problematic. They may be a direct consequence of extensive alcohol intake or only indirectly related to it. The nurse can indicate to the patient that she can help him solve these problems. If the patient responds favorably, the nurse can work out a referral to a specialized treatment facility. It is surprising how few alcoholics in these circumstances balk at the idea of going to a clinic for alcololics, even though alcohol may never have been spoken about by patient or nurse.

A middle-aged man was hospitalized for a flare-up of an arthritic condition. His alcoholism came to light when his wife asked a nurse if heavy drinking could aggravate arthritis. The patient himself never mentioned drinking and, confronted with his wife's rather lengthy documentation of his drinking problem, he minimized it, saying on the one hand that he drank a six-pack watching TV on weekends and on the other that his wife, coming as she did from an abstemious background, considered any alcohol consumption excessive. The matter was not pursued further by ward personnel, but the patient became fond of a nurse and complained to her in detail how his wife nagged him; at the same time he confessed that he didn't treat her as he should and that he egged her on to anger. When he spoke of his desire to control his nastiness toward his wife, the nurse mentioned that she knew where he could get help with his problem. He expressed interest, and she told him to call the alcohol clinic when he was discharged. He showed neither surprise nor reluctance and subsequently called the clinic and entered treatment. Later the wife came to the clinic herself and said that he continued to drink heavily, but less frequently, and that he was less often abusive to her under the influence of alcohol. The focus of treatment in the clinic was on the marriage, and drinking came up only as an incidental issue.

The caretaker must also be prepared, especially with counter-dependent deniers, to find no problems other than the specific one for which he sought aid in the first place: the broken limb, the allergic reaction, or the disability payment. Here a relationship of interest and kindness that may pave the way for future contacts can be offered.

The industrial health worker is in a different position, since he usually must invoke company rules and regulations about continuance of employment. Although varying from company to company, the typical choice offered to the alcoholic has a salutary effect: the alcoholic employee stops drinking in ways that impair job performance, or goes into treatment for his problem, or terminates his employment. Ordinarily, a probationary period accompanies the choice. Most workers accept treatment; few lose their jobs, suggesting that drinking that affects job performance is reduced. It is not known whether a more comprehensive effect on the worker's total life situation occurs.

Often the caretaker is faced with an alcoholic who comes to him under duress. A clergyman, for example, is asked to talk with an alcoholic who doesn't wish to see him, but who comes because his wife threatens to initiate separation proceedings. The clergyman carefully makes clear to the husband that the choice about seeing him is the husband's own and that he, the minister, is not taking sides about separation. To give a counterdependent alcoholic no alternative is too great a challenge to his façade. Even so, the alcoholic is likely to feel that he is under compulsion to see the caretaker. The major importance about the question of choice occurs in later stages of contact, when the alcoholic insists that he comes, and has been coming, to see the clergyman against his will. Then the caretaker's pre-established position enables him to point out that the patient comes to see him on his own, a matter decided in their first meeting. If choice is not given early, the patient is later apt to use the omission as an excuse to flee from a rehabilitative relation.

In this chapter we have examined denial in the alcoholic as varying between the extremes of psychotic and normal denial, and while the alcoholic relies extensively on the mechanism, he does so neither psychotically nor normally. The connection between denial and the handling of dependent needs shows that denial is less necessary for dependent than for counterdependent and dependent-independent alcoholics. But the fact that dependent alcoholics deny less does not mean that they progress more in treatment. The breakdown of denial is not always necessary for successful treatment, as some suppose.

5

IMPULSIVITY AND FRUSTRATION

PSYCHOANALYTIC WRITERS generally classify alcoholism as one of the impulse disorders, along with other addictions, kleptomania, pyromania, compulsive eating, and so on. The hallmark of the impulse disorder is that the afflicted individual must act on an impulse or wish as it arises; when the impulse is not immediately gratified, the individual suffers extreme anxiety. For alcoholics, the wish that demands satiation is the impulse to drink. As we shall see, however, his need to act impulsively is not confined solely to the consumption of liquor, but is a generalized personality trait that permeates much of the alcoholic's behavior. But first, what is the general relation between impulses and their in-action expression?

We all have impulses, wishes, needs, desires to execute certain actions, but we make many complicated decisions about the wishes we will act on and those we will not: these decisions involve timing, sequence, appropriateness, and the particular situation we are in. There is a whole set of rules and conditions, seemingly inbred, about how we will and will not satisfy the insistencies of our needs. These rules and conditions are learned from infancy on. The "naturalness" that we invest in them comes about because of the ordinarily automatic way in which they come into play and because of our unawareness of their operation, except when our attention is directed toward them.

The satisfaction of the wish to eat may serve as an illustrative example. The foods we eat, their preparation, the time at which we consume them, the utensils we use, all are learned responses, far from "natural" in the sense of gratification of a biological need. The learning itself is a psychological process, but the content of what is learned is based in large part on social and cultural demands. The need to eat is channeled differently in different societies. Within these channels is a considerable range in what is considered to be acceptable eating behavior. Behaviors that occur outside the range are usually judged to be odd or peculiar. To eat a full-course dinner upon arising and breakfast upon retiring, for example, would be thought of as strange, although there is no reason in nature why such a judgment should be made.

When the learning, or socialization, process is faulty, the individual will have difficulties in expressing or inhibiting his impulses in ways acceptable to the society he lives in. Socialization, by the way, is the process of learning how to become an accepted member of any particular society or culture. The socialization of eating behavior is obviously different between an American child and the child of a Bantu tribesman. Inadequate socialization in areas such as food, elimination, and dress is rare indeed, except where the individual has a basic disturbance in his capacity to learn, as in the case of a severely mentally retarded child. In other areas of behavior, especially those viewed with mixed emotions, inadequate or faulty socialization is not uncommon; in our society these include the socialization of sexual, aggressive, and dependent drives. And it is in behavior involving these drives that socially unacceptable acts predominate. Inhibitory mechanisms are often either too strong or too weak; if the former, we have a neurotic disorder; if the latter, an impulse disorder. In the impulse disorder, the individual has failed to learn well how to inhibit, delay, or to seek substitute forms of satisfaction in lieu of direct and immediate gratification of internal wishes.

With the alcoholic, this imperfect socialization is intimately linked to dependent wishes, and resulting problems are particularly severe in light of the character of dependency in its early infantile form. Dependency in the infant, as many psychoanalysts have observed, consists of a state of being loved, of receiving without conditions and without exerting oneself. The infant makes little distinction between himself and the external source of satisfaction for his needs: he and the source of satisfaction are magically one, and to wish is to be satisfied. For the infant to come to know that he must give of himself, that he must do things in order to receive, and that he does not have absolute control over the fount of gratification is the first painful lesson of his life. To some, it matters not that they can satisfy themselves in wish fulfillment, the forerunner of daydreaming and later of planning—for this is only a partial fulfillment, an insubstantial reflection of direct and immediate granting of a wish. Alcoholics never completely learn this painful lesson, and in adulthood the wish for the fairy godmother who gives all reappears when dependent needs are intense. This is what is meant when it is said that the alcoholic seeks nirvana through alcohol, a condition in which all needs are gratified through wishing without action. The failure of the alcoholic to learn to satisfy dependent needs in indirect as well as direct ways makes it easier to understand the intensity of his dependent needs and his difficulty in tolerating delays of expressing and thereby gratifying his wishes.

One may ask why the alcoholic fails to learn how to modulate dependency needs so that they do not dominate him. Both psychological theorists of human learning and psychoanalysts have at least partial answers to this question. From experiments with animals and observational studies of small children, the learning theorists conclude that if a drive is frustrated, its strength increases, so long as frustration doesn't go beyond biological tolerance. A hungry man becomes hungrier if he is not fed, but he dies if he is never fed. Similarly, the dependent needs of an infant who is infrequently caressed, cuddled, and otherwise attended become more, rather than less, intense; if, however, deprivation of loving care is markedly severe, the baby will literally wither away and eventually die, as studies of institutionalized, but physically unloved, infants have demonstrated. The analysts substantially agree with the learning theorists on these points, but they add that a surfeit of attention or sharp alternation between deprivation and gratification can similarly fix a pattern of dependency. Whether infants who have been deprived, satiated, or alternately gratified and frustrated become alcoholic depends on many factors, but a necessary ingredient in becoming alcoholic is intense dependency needs.

The alcoholic who has just been frustrated feels like the baby whose favorite toy is taken from him. His capacity to withstand frustration is slight indeed. The technical sobriquet of this phenomenon is low frustration tolerance. When the alcoholic is denied a wish, request, desire, or demand, he becomes inwardly enraged; outwardly, he may be deferential, withdrawing, insistent, or angry. But inwardly he is furious. Most of us can put things off for a bit, sometimes even under conditions of extreme frustration, but to the alcoholic, delay and tolerance are anathema.

A man with an alcohol problem had an obscure, somewhat painful but not dangerous ailment, for which he required the services of a specialist. Given the name of a doctor, he called to find he could not get an appointment until three weeks later. He demanded to speak with the doctor, to whom he described his unbearable pain; the doctor thereupon instructed his secretary to squeeze the man in the next day. The patient came in on schedule, waited for fifteen minutes, then asked the secretary when he would be seen. She explained that the doctor was running behind schedule, and the patient would have to wait a few minutes longer. A few moments later, he left in indignation, had a couple of drinks, and then went to a general physician, who gave him a pain-killer for relief of his symptoms.

The alcoholic interprets ordinary frustrations not in terms of reality but as direct personal rejections. This reaction occurs in the most mundane situations: being waited on in a restaurant, having to wait for an ordered drink, being stuck in traffic, and so on. Minor irritants to most of us become major catastrophes to the alcoholic. It is not difficult to imagine how his resulting responses, oft repeated, affect relations with family, friends, and fellow employees. Impatience and unreflective action by the alcoholic vary according to whether he is dependent, counterdependent, or dependent-independent in his behavioral orientation.

The dependent alcoholic generally is impulsive and unable to tolerate the blocking of his desires. Nevertheless, with benevolent authorities he is less prone to act on impulse and appears to handle frustration more flexibly. His relation to authority serves to gratify dependency needs: even when he is frustrated by an authority, his inner assumption is that the authority is benevolent and interested in him. The dependent alcoholic who seeks help usually relates to caretakers submissively, placing them in the role of the authoritative expert. His submission may assume different forms, ranging from passive compliance to servile obsequiousness, but he tends to follow "orders." He will sometimes wait for inordinately long periods of time to see a social worker or doctor.

This highly dependent attitude toward authority is achieved at some cost to the alcoholic, since he submerges other conflicting feelings. First, part of his dependent attitude toward authority is based on fear of what might happen if he didn't go along with it. Next, he suppresses angry feelings that occur in response to any frustrations the person in charge imposes upon him. Fear and resentment are revealed by his servility and obsequiousness and by the often nagging quality of his requests. Whenever the alcoholic makes clear to you how wonderful he feels you are, you can be certain that he is covering up a good deal of angry feeling toward you.

Dependent wishes are gratified by benevolent authorities so

that the alcoholic has less push to act on impulse and is less sensitive to supposed slights. We have seen earlier how well dependent alcoholics do in the armed forces and other situations where their needs are provided and where the environment has an unambiguous structure. Anger toward authority rarely manifests itself directly, but in the Army or Navy setting it comes out in gripe sessions, or in relation to caretakers in other indirect forms. A common example is the patient who in his early contacts with you answers your questions with "Yes, sir" and "No, sir," and who at the end of the interview thanks you for your help as he leaves. Unless the hostility that underlies his dependence is dealt with immediately, the patient soon fails to keep his appointments, though when you call him he says he will certainly be there the next time. This kind of passive resistance is often found among alcoholics.

When the relation between the caretaker and dependent alcoholic is an ongoing affair, the alcoholic eventually reveals his inability to withstand frustration over a prolonged period. If, for example, the alcoholic is kept waiting on one occasion, he will at the time have no apparent refractory reaction: he understands and doesn't complain. On the next occasion, however, he may do one of several things: keep you waiting, not show up at all, call and ask that the appointment time be changed, or ask to see you more frequently. All of these reflect his dependent attachment to you, and also indicate his anger at you for frustrating him and for permitting him to be dependent on you in the first place.

Since these processes are unspoken, unconscious, and accompanied by an almost impenetrable screen of passivity, they are difficult to bring to light so that caretaker and patient can examine them together. To help the dependent alcoholic to see that fear and hostility form a major, underlying aspect of his relations to you is a formidable task.

Another common feature of the dependent alcoholic in relation to authorities is his dependent, usually unconscious belief that the caretaker possesses a magical formula to bring about an immediate and beneficial change in him. This belief originates in the qualities the alcoholic attributed to his mother when he was an infant: the source of all good things and of all fulfillment. Since the caretaker is not a magician, fulfillment of the fantasy is patently impossible, and the relation between caretaker and patient may be doomed to failure unless the caretaker takes steps to neutralize the patient's belief in his omnipotence. When the patient is able to see and appreciate that there may be nonmagical ways in which the caretaker can help the alcoholic, a giant step toward health has been taken. Unfortunately, the alcoholic's fantasy is often not verbalized, but serves as an unspoken backdrop against which the explicit but relatively unimportant transactions between caretaker and patient take place. When the patient leaves, he is unsatisfied and unfulfilled and may decide that he has not gotten what he wanted from the caretaker. He may be inwardly angry at the caretaker for refusing to give him what he is internally certain that the caretaker has, and he may perceive the caretaker as willfully withholding the magic pill that could solve his problems. Under these circumstances, it is rare for the dependent alcoholic to return to see the caretaker again.

Sometimes the situation described above is the beginning of an eventually abortive series of encounters between caretaker and patient. The alcoholic leaves the first meeting unsatisfied and angry, and he acts upon his anger by failing to keep subsequent appointments. As time passes, anger diminishes, and the dependent's perception of the caretaker as an omnipotent benefactor is again on the ascendant. Once again the alcoholic seeks out the caretaker, and the process repeats itself. Unless the caretaker points out to the alcoholic what he is doing, this cyclic, nontherapeutic relation may continue for a long time. Another variation of this pattern: the alcoholic has an array of caretakers in his environment and goes from one to the other in the hope that one of them will not withhold his magic.

The search for help that is so dominated by fantasies of fulfillment that they obscure sincere requests for help aids us to understand the patient who has tried Alcoholics Anonymous, antabuse, a home for alcoholics, his local physician, and so on, to no avail. The search, continually frustrated, is not for help in the caretaker's terms, but for aid and succor based on an inner wish to be warmly held and comforted. The caretaker who explicitly knows the help he has to offer and how he renders it can assess in initial encounters whether his help is what the alcoholic needs and wants. He can tell the alcoholic what he is able and unable to do. This explicit approach clarifies the relation for both parties, undercuts the patient's fantasies of magic fulfillment, and may avoid an eventually abortive situation. Certainly, when the caretaker's expectations diverge completely from the alcoholic's, and this divergence is not brought to light, one can hope for little from the relationship.

Unlike the dependent alcoholic, the counterdependent alcoholic quickly reveals his inability to tolerate the least frustration by his impulsive and frequently resentful responses to it. Often, he stands on his dignity, assuming an attitude of "How dare you treat me this way!" like the man whom the doctor kept waiting. We have seen in an earlier chapter how difficult it is for this alcoholic to come voluntarily to a caretaking setting, particularly for a problem that is directly and inescapably related to his unhealthy use of alcohol. When he does place himself in such a situation, he will expend great amounts of energy in the attempt to terminate the relation without losing face, in a manner that he can justify to himself as reasonable.

An alcoholic with a history of hypermasculine behavior entered psychotherapy when his fiancée threatened to break off their engagement. He did well and eventually got married, but near the end of treatment it came out that he entered therapy not for himself, but as he put it, "I had to pamper her—you know how women are." Another man, faced with entering therapy or losing his position as senior accountant in a large firm, began treatment; he soon gave up drinking, and so no longer faced the prospect of losing his job. He nevertheless continued in therapy with the reason that his employer forced him to do so.

The counterdependent alcoholic's view of authority is basically similar to that of the dependent alcoholic, but is defended against so as to make his behavior distinctly different from that of the dependent alcoholic. Basically fearful of authority, he handles this fear by denying its existence, or by challenging it, or by attempting to usurp authority wherever he sees it. He is on guard to see that authority does not encroach on his independence; his vigilance is an indication of the instability of his independent strivings. The truly independent man is not preoccupied with the possibility that his autonomy will be infringed upon.

One man invariably and immediately called superiors by their first names, and another made his immediate boss laugh by caustically witty comments about their unit manager. Counterdependent alcoholics are frequently critical of the way you conduct an interview and inform you how it should be done. One patient I had mentally listed and graded the reactions I might have to any situation he brought up in therapy; he then scored my response to see whether I lived up to his standards of the good therapist. It later came out he thereby neutralized my authority.

The counterdependent alcoholic's fear of a dependent relation, his inability to tolerate frustration, and his fear of being engulfed by authority conspire to make him hypersensitively ready to flee the caretaking setting. He is like a colt that has never been ridden. He does not tolerate the slightest period of waiting, and his demands must be fulfilled now. He seizes upon a rebuff or slight as an occasion to provoke a contretemps to end a relationship. When we consider the fact that waiting, counterhostility, and moralizing remarks are common experiences for alcoholics, it is not surprising that the alcoholic doesn't have to look far to feel frustrated and slighted. Nevertheless, the childish quality of his behavior is immediately apparent and is one reason why alcoholics are often described as having "infantile," "immature," or "regressed" personalities.

Much of the alcoholic's behavior reminds us of a small child; it is as if he never grew up in the first place or, having grown up fitfully, he returned to earlier, more childlike ways of coping with problems under the stress of adulthood. Children react with rage, temper tantrums, or sullen withdrawal when their wishes are not satisfied on the spot. Part of growing up is learning how to delay gratification and to find substitute means of satisfying wishes that if acted upon directly would result in inappropriate behavior. Building up tolerance for frustration is, in Freud's terms, suffering pain for the sake of later pleasure.

In comparison with dependent and counterdependent alcoholics, the dependent-independent alcoholic shows from a caretaking viewpoint the most difficult behavior in response to frustration, but with a major exception: he has periods of "good" impulse control and capacity to withstand frustration. These islands of relative stability, sometimes flooded by childlike mechanisms, make treatment of the dependent-independent alcoholic potentially rewarding. Depending on variations of internal and external events, he may be vociferous in not tolerating the slightest amount of frustration; he may be docile and submissive, seemingly accepting whatever frustrations confront him; or he may actively and realistically attempt to surmount obstacles in the path leading to a sought-after goal. As we know from our earlier discussions, the contradictions in his behavior are difficult for caretakers to reconcile.

Paradoxically, his inconsistencies allow us to help him to understand what he is doing, what he hopes to gain by it, and whether he does it out of preference or out of compulsion. Analysis of contradictions in his behavior enable him to see how responses of rage or withdrawal or standing on his dignity block him from achieving other goals. He enters treatment for at least two reasons:

to receive the touch of the magic wand that will make him well and to understand himself to a point where alcohol will no longer be his *raison d'être*. Able to see that the first reason is specious, he will be more able to devote himself to the second. Because he is able to permit himself more conscious pain than other alcoholics, the dependent-independent alcoholic is more open to self-examination, with the additional incentive of desiring to rid himself of the burden of anxiety.

The inconsistency of the dependent-independent alcoholic's behavior is a useful tool in therapy. The caretaker wonders with the patient why he was so angry last time over a particular slight, but that this time it doesn't seem to bother him: what are these back-and-forth shifts all about? Periods when the patient is more in control of himself are opportunities to try to understand what goes on inside him when he is less self-controlled.

The swings back and forth between dependency and its denial are well-illustrated by an episode in the long-term treatment of a young man who had been going downhill with alcohol since his early twenties. From the beginning of therapy he wondered why I was interested in him, and it was obvious that he was asking whether I liked him. He had little money for treatment, and the nature of his job made his financial status uncertain, so I told him that I would see him even if he had no money as long as his financial situation was not the result of his own actions. He scoffed at my comments. Some months later he lost his job, not because of an anticipated and routine layoff, but because he took more than the allotted time for lunch, despite repeated warnings. Around this time his feelings of trust, liking, and faith were becoming intense. As we discussed his dismissal, it became evident to both of us that he had provoked being fired. At the same time he expected, indeed demanded, that I continue to see him for nothing. He did not recall the proviso that I would see him free if he had done nothing to bring about his impecunious condition. I told him that I would see him another month for no fee, but that I would not continue to see him after that unless he found a job. He became furious, saying that my actions proved I was untrustworthy, undependable, and a liar; that he could stand on his own two feet and didn't need me; and that I was just out for his money. I held to my decision, he failed to get a new job, and therapy ended on a bitter note. Three months later he called, saying that he wanted to resume treatment; he had had a job for most of the time he had discontinued treatment. He finally decided that his need to do something about himself was greater than a minor disagreement with me. We continued on, he did well in therapy, but held to the end a conviction, softened it is true, that I had stopped therapy because he was unable to pay for it.

An aspect of impulsivity not yet touched upon is the relation between impulsivity, low tolerance of frustration, and drinking behavior. Whatever the pattern of drinking behavior, regular or episodic, impulsivity exerts a prominent and decisive influence. Many alcoholics claim they control their drinking, and that may indeed appear to be the case. Some alcoholics, for example, do not begin to drink until a certain time of day, but then drink until stuporous. Such "controlled" drinking merely shows that a person has a modicum of capacity to delay impulses; close examination reveals that during the day the person's inner fantasies and thoughts are taken up with the time when he will take his first drink of the day and that, as this time approaches, the fantasies dominate consciousness. When blocked from drinking at the usual time, he becomes anxious, irritable, and depressed. This drinker typically advances the usual time bit by bit so that it gradually comes earlier in the day. Like other daydreams, those about drinking take up time and energy and can have the net effect of reducing efficiency in work or whatever else one is doing.

Most alcoholics drink directly on impulse, following a real or apparent impediment to their desires. Many observers see drinking-on-impulse as a variation of "any excuse will serve the occasion." Perhaps this view is an oversimplification. That he constantly seeks reasons to justify the need for alcohol does not mean that an alcoholic does not also drink in response to frustration. The danger in assuming that alcoholics invariably seek out any excuse to drink is that it leads to moral judgments about alcoholics that are not in their best interests and are certainly beside the point. The alcoholic unquestionably has a basic urge to drink, and he undoubtedly tries to justify to himself and others satisfaction of this insistent inner demand. Nevertheless, the patterning of drinking follows upon external events and inner states that the alcoholic perceives as hopelessly frustrating. In treatment, one must attempt to uncover underlying continuities that bind each of these precipitating events together, rather than to focus on their concrete nature. The alcoholic drinks not because he lost a sales account, but because that loss triggered off feelings of futility and worthlessness, feelings just as easily mobilized by his four-year-old son saying, "I hate you!" or by his getting a flat tire.

Drinking on impulse or in response to frustration is, of course, not the sole province of alcoholics and is common enough among social drinkers. But at least three differences exist between pathological and nonpathological impulsive drinking. The person without an alcoholic problem infrequently drinks on impulse, whereas the alcoholic does so routinely and frequently. Next, the social-impulse drinker imbibes at socially accepted and relevant places and times; he would not, for example, sneak a drink on the job. More typically, after a frustrating day or incident, he will drink when he comes home. The context in which he drinks and his aim in drinking are not self-harmful, as is characteristic of the alcoholic. He drinks to gain momentary surcease from feelings aroused by a frustrating event which he believes himself unable to control. Finally, his impulsive drinking is controlled because he does not have to drink to inebriety or unconsciousness to achieve his aim. Impulse drinking in the nonalcoholic may be viewed as an instance of what some psychoanalysts have called "regression in the service of the ego." Drinking serves to act as a balm to a wounded ego, allowing it respite and exerting a curative effect. Impulsive drinking in the alcoholic, on the other hand, represents a regression that harms rather than recharges the ego. Once started, the alcoholic cannot control drinking. It thereby exerts a progressively disintegrative effect on the executive functions of his personality.

Because he has little capacity to withstand frustration, the alcoholic has great difficulty in keeping to rules and regulations, since rules by their very nature involve frustration, however minimal. Violation of rules disturbs caretakers and disrupts the organization, efficiency, and morale of a ward or clinic. The common response to broken rules is punishment, yet some caretakers go to the opposite extreme of changing regulations for alcoholics but not for other patients—or of being highly permissive. Where services are extended to others besides alcoholics, changing rules just for alcoholics is as much an error as a punitive orientation. Both mean to the alcoholic that he is little understood, and he trusts permissive no more than punitive persons. He needs and seeks controls and limits, even as he perceives them as frustrations against which he must struggle. Once again he reminds us of a child. In ambiguous situations he repeatedly breaks rules to force their redefinition so that their limits and sanctions are crystal clear. Limits have to be set and adhered to; when the alcoholic comes to accept that he will not be punished for exceeding limits, he less often finds it necessary to exceed them. For instance, in psychotherapy the patient will not be seen if he comes to an interview intoxicated; at the same time therapy will not be terminated because he comes to interviews intoxicated.

For example, a spree drinker refused all medical, psychiatric, or other treatment when drinking. If hospitalized, he would leave against the advice of doctor and hospital, signing the necessary papers to absolve them of responsibility. His wife, increasingly and realistically concerned that he might injure himself during a debauch, finally took legal action to have him committed to a hospital. When he became aware of these proceedings, he failed to fight them as expected; later he said that commitment was a relief because he knew that at last he was protected from himself.

In dealing with alcoholics in caretaking settings, awareness of their diminished capacity to withstand frustration can be an important guide in helping them. Waiting and delays are inevitable. To explain to the alcoholic when he will have to wait and why is often an effective antidote to anger or withdrawal. Also, there is always a certain amount of red tape that may seem to the patient completely unrelated to his needs and wishes, as it often is. Explanations about the necessity to the organization of filling out forms and answering questions may serve to reduce the impersonality and meaninglessness that characterize such confrontations.

Where the alcoholic is the only kind of patient, the institution may be organized so that rules and regulations take into account the fact that alcoholics have an incompletely developed system of controls over their impulses. Potential frustrations can be held to a minimum, and nonobservance of rules need not result in punitive or rejecting stances by caretakers. For example, no drinking in the institution is a definite rule; its observance meets with approval, its nonobservance with disapproval. Yet drinking and intoxication do not result in expulsion from the institution. Expulsion under these circumstances is a frequent policy in most inpatient facilities. We must, however, provide a milieu conducive to growth. This environment tolerates extremes in infractions of regulations, just as parents do in rearing their children. The medium of psychological growth in the family consists of approval or disapproval by the parents for particular actions; the effectiveness of positive and negative sanctions depends on the extent of the attachment the child has for his parents. In inpatient settings the alcoholic must have a similar, if rudimentary, relation to the institution or to a particular person in it. Only under these circumstances can positive and negative sanctions, approval and disapproval, produce psychological growth in a group-living setting. In addition, in an atmosphere which simulates to some degree conditions of early family life, the alcoholic should have the opportunity of regularly discussing with one person the meanings of actions and feelings as they relate to childhood events and feelings.

Finally, inpatient facilities for alcoholics have the opportunity to build in a system of rewards that will tend to strengthen the alcoholic's capacity to control his behavior. The mechanics of such a system can operate in various ways. For example, rewards, such as special privileges, can be given for approved behavior; this does not necessarily mean an invariant withdrawal of privileges for disapproved behavior. Halfway houses, for example, with individual rooms and dormitory arrangements may give rooms to those who do not slip. Introducing a spirit of competition for privileges is useful, especially when it takes into account individual differences in capacity to compete. Above all, in any program of rehabilitation, practices, procedures, and goals are carefully explained and described to each patient and their specific relevance to him spelled out concretely.

In this chapter, we have attempted to understand why impulsivity and difficulty in tolerating frustration are characteristic of alcoholics. We examined their relation to dependency needs and saw how their expression varies with the alcoholic's method of coping with underlying needs to depend on others. The intimate connection between impulsivity, inability to tolerate frustration, and drinking behavior per se was explored. Finally, we examined how caretakers may best approach alcoholics with respect to the reduction of responses to frustration that lead to abortive rehabilitative alliances.

77

6

OVER- AND UNDER-EVALUATION OF THE SELF

THE ESTEEM in which the alcoholic holds himself reflects both his fantasies of omnipotence and his feelings of worthlessness. His self-regard is alternately or simultaneously extremely high or low. An explanation of this paradox requires that we examine self-esteem and its development in humans.

One of the infant's earliest psychological certainties is that he is the center of the world, indeed *the* world. His every wish is a command. This attitude of psychological omnipotence is commonly referred to as egocentrism and by the psychoanalysts as primary narcissism. In it, the infant is presumed to be all-powerful, so powerful that the taking of action to obtain goals is unnecessary; mere wishing demands gratification, and he is, therefore, the passive recipient of all good things. This is a completely internal mental state that has only accidental congruence with reality. The infant does not view his situation as others do, since his perceptual, motoric, and other functions are insufficiently developed for him to be aware of himself as a person distinct from others or his environment. In fact, he is physically helpless and completely dependent on others in every facet of his existence. That maternal care ordinarily provides immediate satisfaction for all his needs, especially those for food, warmth, and comfort, tends in some degree to reinforce a primitive attitude of omnipotence and egocentrism.

As he grows physically, the infant gradually comes to tell one need from another and to realize that the sources of gratification of his needs are largely outside himself and that he *is* dependent on them. He becomes increasingly aware of how small, helpless, and impotent he is. The more helpless the infant, the greater his sense of omnipotence, while as he becomes less helpless and more able to indicate his needs to others, his sense of omnipotence gradually begins to diminish.

These two basic attitudes are stages that we go through in the first year or two of life. Their residue, however, remains with us throughout life: in childhood, adolescence, adulthood, and old age. As we grow and mature, we of course learn that we are not all-powerful, and that our wishes are not always-to-be-obeyed commands. We learn to modulate the satisfaction of our needs through delay and substitution, so that the modes of satisfaction are consonant with the dictates of our environment. Similarly, we become aware that we are not helpless beings without means to exercise control over ourselves or others, but, within social limits, effective determiners of our destiny.

At times of later crisis, we may re-experience early feelings, attitudes, and dispositions of omnipotence and helplessness. When the attitude is egocentric omnipotence, we may feel, despite reality, that we are in complete command, that we are great, and that all we wish is or will be fulfilled. We overvalue ourselves and our capacities; in the extreme, such feelings express themselves in a state of manic excitement. When the disposition is helplessness, we devalue ourselves with a claim of being totally helpless and without resources; we are certain that our wishes carry no weight and will fail to be fulfilled; and we are convinced of our worthlessness and badness. In the extreme instance, dominance of these feelings reflects severe depression. The direction which response to crisis takes will depend on the specific balance of psychological forces that were established when we were small or that were modified by experiences occurring during later growth.

These early preverbal attitudes play a more prominent role for some individuals than for others and thus influence subsequent psychological development more. For some, they predispose to subsequent conflict and difficulty. Certainly, this appears to be true for alcoholics. All-powerful feelings on the one hand and helpless feelings on the other are features of a child's dependent relation to his environment. In these early stages the alcoholic's proclivities to overvalue himself are born. We do not know precisely why attitudes of omnipotence and impotence (not to be understood in its sexual meaning, but as a sense of personal inadequacy, a feeling of being unequipped to exert any significant impact on the environment or other persons) persist in the alcoholic, nor the exact conditions which permit their development. But we can make some pretty fair guesses.

We have assumed that the alcoholic's needs for unconditional love are very strong. The pressure and insistence of these needs likely lead the alcoholic to yearn to return to a time in which he fantasies complete fulfillment. Add to his yearning the inevitable, natural frustration of dependency: he was not always nurtured and loved without conditions. He interpreted these frustrations as personal rejections, as well as evidence that he was not omnipotent. Many individuals, alcoholics among them, attempt to rationalize being rejected with explanations that may or may not coincide with actual circumstances. A common rationale of late infancy and early childhood is that one is bad and so deserves rejection. While the nature of badness varies from person to person, it is usually intimately connected with either angry or sexual feelings. Time and again in therapy, patients associate internal states of worthlessness with infantile and guilt-provoking fantasies of destruction or infantile masturbation, both of which parents ordinarily reprimand. In the alcoholic the sense of badness is so pervasive as actually to permanently cripple his regard for himself.

A critical ingredient of the alcoholic-in-the-making is the way in which his parents behaved toward him. Evidence shows that parents, particularly mothers, of alcoholics are either emotionally depriving or at the other extreme overindulgent. Depriving mothers range from cool indifference to active rejection and neglect of their children. Deprivation increases needs to be dependent. Overindulgent mothers, on the other hand, give the child a sense that he never has to lift a finger to help himself, which encourages and fixes attitudes of infantile omnipotence.

Secondary processes complicate the situation further. It is a rare person who is willing or able to admit to himself that he feels impotent and inferior. To avoid such painful admissions, the alcoholic represses or denies feelings of inadequacy, along with needs to be dependent, and adopts in their place a counterattitude of superiority and worthiness. This goes hand in glove with already strong dispositions toward primitive omnipotence. And in the background is the desire to return to an infantile state of passive freedom and recipiency, seen as the means of escape from frustrations and anxieties of responsible adulthood, and a return to lost warmth and security.

An openly dependent alcoholic is readier than others to admit feelings of worthlessness and lack of capacity. His admissions are closely related to his use of denial. Avowals of inferiority and helplessness are more attempts to obtain dependent supplies in the form of sympathy and attention than true facing of feelings of inadequacy. What better way to be recognized than to present oneself as sorely in need of help to those whose profession it is to help? When one comes to know a dependent alcoholic, the subtle justifications of his freely admitted inability to achieve or get along with others become more apparent than one might have supposed from a first meeting. In the last analysis his justifications amount to this: he is a victim of capricious external circumstance.

The dependent alcoholic has a layering effect with regard to feelings of inferiority and superiority. The most superficial level is avowed inadequacy (which has as one of its aims the eliciting of sympathetic attention); the next level is self-justification combined with superiority; and, finally, there are deep-seated and painful feelings of helplessness and inadequacy. It is easy to mislead ourselves to consider the process one of conscious control and thereby to adopt a common-sense attitude that says, "How ridiculous! Why doesn't he just get hold of himself and stop this nonsense?" Easier said than done. Not only is the process beyond the alcoholic's control, but usually he is unaware of what he is doing, except in gross terms. Part of psychotherapy with alcoholics (as well as others) is to help them to become aware of what they do and what they feel. Only after self-recognition occurs is one able to transform or to transcend oneself—and self-recognition in itself is a lengthy business.

The level of self-justification may take several forms alone or in combination. Alcoholics commonly speak of their unrealized capacities and potentialities. For instance, an alcoholic will tell you how well he could have done educationally or occupationally, but he had to go to work when he was very young to help support the family; or that a blossoming career was cut short by the advent of the war and the necessity of military service; or that a promising business was ruined through the malfeasance of a partner; or that offers of a professional athletic future were terminated by a physical infirmity. Such examples may be given ad infinitum. I am always impressed by two things in these accounts: the outside source of frustration and the self-glorification. Those who work with alcoholics have noted unrealized talents and gifts in many of their clients. Such revelations should be taken with a grain of salt: it is not that they do not reflect reality, but that in relating them, the alcoholic is saying things and asking things that are irrelevant to reality. He is telling you that he is a good and capable guy, and he is trying to assure you that he doesn't feel inadequate; he is asking you to like him and to sympathize with his misfortunes. We can agree with him, tendering our sympathy and respect for an individual with unique assets and abilities, but we musn't be misled by attempts to draw us away from feelings of inadequacy. If we permit ourselves to be misled, the alcoholic will be grateful, but only temporarily, because he knows deep down that we don't fully understand him.

In addition to the theme of unrealized capacities are two others, martyrdom and victimization by malignant fate. The martyred alcoholic gave up everything, himself included, for a higher aim like living with an aged mother after father died and other children left home; giving oneself over to an employer in the interests of seeing the business grow, but never getting one's just rewards; or dedicating oneself and one's time to a volunteer organization. The central feature is the alcoholic's complete devotion of self and time to someone or something else, so that he never had an opportunity to do what he really wanted or to look after himself. The dependency and masochism are only too apparent, as is ever-present, but rarely verbalized, resentment.

The victimized alcoholic feels that he is the unwitting prey of those around him. For example, an alcoholic's father wouldn't allow him to further his education, but insisted he go into the family business where his talents were wasted; or he was destined to be a writer, but because of his wife's importunities he had to give up his career for something less worthy. These justifications are presented without regard to what the individual has or has not done in his life. The frustrated writer may, for example, be a highly successful executive in an advertising agency; the man forced into his father's business may have done well at it; or the potential athlete may have many other accomplishments to his credit. The fact that the alcoholic perceives himself as inadequate and must justify himself by unreal inadequacies in spite of real success demonstrates the extraordinary strength and power of underlying feelings of helplessness and impotence.

The dependent alcoholic's avowals of inferiority serve to gain attention and sympathy and are also a subtle way of avoiding awareness of the depth of feelings of worthlessness. He hopes his candor will lead others to focus on less painful areas of his existence. The counterdependent alcoholic reveals a far different picture in surface behavior.

The counterdependent alcoholic betrays the presence of feelings of inferiority by emphasizing superiority. As with many aspects of his personality, he protests too much. The counterdependent alcoholic acts as if he assumes that it is his right to get preferential treatment in life, that the satisfaction of his needs and desires comes before that of others. He behaves, further, as though he were different and above others, that it is self-evident that his special status in life means special treatment from those he knows and meets. He is wary of possible infringements on his dignity as a human being and on his rights. This often lends to the counterdependent alcoholic a touchiness which those around him find most difficult to go beyond.

Another way he demonstrates his superiority is by indicating his importance, either directly or borrowed through his association with prominent and influential individuals. He may dwell on past accomplishments and exploits or tell you of a politician or artist or professor, a close friend of his. His intimate connections with prominent people vicariously gain him prominence. With some alcoholics such behavior is smoothly articulated with the rest of their personality; with some it degenerates into an attitude of self-importance and aggrandizement which embarrasses and alienates those around him.

Self-importance varies with sobriety. Many men, when sober, would never dream of talking about social connections; when drunk, however, they may impress upon friends and acquaintances the significance of their relations with socially prominent people. A patient of mine from an upper-class background disgusts himself because he lords it over less-socially-advantaged companions when he is drinking.

In contrast to the dependent alcoholic who emphasizes his inadequacies, but attempts to justify them, the counterdependent alcoholic focuses on real or illusory accomplishments and will rarely admit to inadequacy. His façade of hyperadequacy patently serves a defensive function for him, but it betrays the very thing he guards from expression: underlying feelings of worthlessness and inadequacy.

The sense of adequacy that counterdependent alcoholics hope to convey is a relatively conventional adolescent view of masculinity: emphasis on physical prowess, daring, bravery, courage, the unusual. The emphasis is invariably on *the* exploit that reflects the self victorious against barely surmountable odds. Although images vary, they ordinarily have to do with sexual, aggressive, or athletic daring and achievement. War experiences supply a ready fund of anecdotal material.

The fact that accomplishments related happened earlier in the individual's life serves several purposes; most germane here is that the incident is not open to verification, since it occurred in the past. And so the alcoholic can elaborate it not only to improve the story, but to increase opportunities for self-enhancement. Fish stories have some basis in fact, but we commonly add frills: colorful details and inches to please both listener and teller. With the counterdependent alcoholic, however, the model for his stories of past accomplishments is the tale of the fish that got away: you can't check it.

Another function such stories serve has to do with the social context in which they are narrated: usually with other men, often while drinking. Mutual exchange of stories serves to cement interpersonal ties and strengthens the member who feels weakest. Ordinarily, this is a positive and integrative function; for the alcoholic, however, it often adds little to his self-esteem because his relations with others are so tenuous.

The counterdependent alcoholic tends to avoid situations which he perceives as tests of his adequacy. In his job, for instance, he may not do as well as he can for fear of failure—a blow to his esteem from which he could not easily recover. Alcoholics in general and counterdependent alcoholics in particular rarely go all out in what they do, unable to stand the possibility of failure inherent in testing the limits of their capacity. At the same time, inner awareness of a fear of striving, a defensive need to hold back, further feeds underlying feelings of inferiority and lack of self-respect.

A counterdependent alcoholic is prone to make extravagant promises. When they are not fulfilled, the alcoholic is embarrassed, feels exposed, and ends up drinking. Usually the promise is a self-enhancing prediction when chances of fulfillment are remote. For example, the alcoholic salesman will tell you, in all inner sincerity, about the million dollar contract he expects to close shortly, or the new patient will assure you that he has at last seen the light and will never drink again. When, as so often happens, he fails to get the contract or he does drink again, it is a source of embarrassed discomfiture, if not severe guilt, that further undermines his already tenuous self-esteem. The tendency toward premature optimism is hardly unique to alcoholics but is a time-honored and universal human frailty. For the alcoholic, however, it can be a pathological behavior because he cannot exercise control over it, and its consequences devastate an already injured sense of self-respect. Many alcoholics are fully convinced of their predictions when they make them, but others know they are verbally inflating a remote chance to a virtual certainty. The latter suffer in the act of predicting, knowing beforehand that the prediction is highly unlikely to come true. They perhaps sense that they won't let it come true, but are unable to forego the momentary opportunity for immediately rewarded self-aggrandizement, empty as they really know it to be, or the chance to hurt themselves in this way.

Exaggerated but self-conscious promising occurs perhaps even

86

more frequently with the dependent-independent alcoholic. More than the counterdependent, the dependent-independent alcoholic is aware of internal states of being and is more apt to put himself into a disadvantageous psychological position. The dependent-independent alcoholic, unlike the dependent and counterdependent alcoholic, consciously suffers from his awareness of feelings of inferiority. Because of his relative flexibility, he has moments in which he cannot help but torture himself with feeling inadequate, and he compulsively complicates this process by sometimes brightly illuminated insights into the little ways he debases himself in order to assure others, as well as himself, of his adequacy and superiority. He tries of course to avoid these moments of painful self-awareness —sometimes with the help of alcohol. Typical of his public behavior is alternation between moods of superficial criticism of himself and moods of superiority in which he goes to the lengths of the counterdependent alcoholic to impress others. In his anguish, the dependent-independent alcoholic is apt to go on sprees of unparalleled intensity and ferocity. The spree is his special tranquilizing agent for calming the furies that attack him from within.

The caretaker can do much to help reduce the alcoholic's struggle to ward off feelings of worthlessness and personal impotence. The cardinal guide is to treat alcoholics with the respect for human worth, dignity, and individuality that we accord to anyone, and which we wish to have accorded to ourselves. We recognize that each person has his own unique capacities, assets, and training that are right for him as a person, and we expect no one to be able to achieve equally well in every type of endeavor.

Since much of the alcoholic's struggle with inferiority and superiority is fought out in the arena of observable achievement, our discussion applies specifically to the vocational counselor and personnel specialist, as well as to others for whom issues of job and occupation dominate the rehabilitative process. The alcoholic's feelings of inadequacy are woven into the fabric of job plans and

87

activities. We must take pains to determine whether the alcoholic is underselling or overselling himself when he speaks of future goals and past accomplishments. The unemployed alcoholic, for example, often applies for a job below his skills and training. The usual explanation is that the alcoholic is known as a poor employment risk among employers in his line of work because excessive drinking has affected his job performance. Rather than make the rounds again and be rebuffed again, he tries to get work where employers are not so discriminating and where demand is high and supply low. This means menial jobs such as kitchen and restaurant work or transient laboring jobs. Long-term alcoholics who show a beneficial change in their drinking patterns often fear to seek work in the specialty for which they originally trained because they anticipate rejection or fear they have lost their skills. In these instances, the vocational counselor may work with the alcoholic actively, attempting to find employers willing to give the alcoholic a chance, or arranging for retraining programs. The dependent alcoholic usually seeks out the low-level job, although the counter-dependent alcoholic may fall into this group out of necessity, rather than inclination, if he has a reputation as a bad risk.

An interesting and instructive example was provided me by a colleague who saw an alcoholic of many years in treatment. The patient did very well, except that he had no job and no special training for any particular occupation. His friends, who themselves had alcohol problems and most of whom were old-timers in A.A., urged him to take anything he could get: odd jobs, dishwashing, housework. But the patient put them off, insisting that if he did whatever came to hand and could not take pride in his job, he would be worse rather than better off; he said it would be the quickest way to get him back to the bottle. As it turned out, he finally got a job that was not "just anything," learned a complicated trade rapidly, and has been doing well with work, life, and alcohol for several years. Perhaps the adage of many people in A.A. and of some professionals in the field about the necessity of starting over again at the bottom applies to some but not all alcoholics.

A common problem with the counterdependent alcoholic is his proclivity to unrealistic job aspirations. He may inflate past accomplishments in such a manner that were he to obtain the position he sought he would ultimately fail in it. In such instances, the counselor may try to get the alcoholic to modify his aspirations so that they are more consonant with his actual performance. This has to be done cautiously, sticking as closely as possible to facts, so as to avoid in the alcoholic feelings that his veracity is being impugned. Involved is an analysis of the concrete details of the individual's training and specific operations of previous positions.

A somewhat different problem occurs when a man promoted to a position of greater responsibility and authority shows uneven performance accompanied by destructive use of alcohol. The outward signs of acceptance and adequacy implicit in a promotion can create an overt alcohol problem in a latent alcoholic who has problems with self-esteem. Anxiety arises from two concerns. First, dependency conflict may be aggravated if the individual sees the new position as one requiring increased independent, autonomous activity and a complementary decrease in dependent gratifications. Second, if the individual basically feels himself to be inadequate and inferior, with whatever success he has achieved resting on factors outside himself, such as luck, nepotism, or a well-developed capacity for fooling others, then the promotion, with its implication of worth and having to provide a stellar performance, can create severe stress for the individual, who wonders if he can keep up the façade. These "success" neuroses do not necessarily include the arbitrary use of alcohol, but alcohol plays its part sufficiently often to require comment here.

Outside the occupational arena, the caretaker is constantly confronted with a wide variety of indications of the alcoholic's sense of inferiority. His insistence and persistence in trying to get the caretaker to treat him with disrespect and derision is often great. The caretaker must always try to keep before himself the knowledge that the alcoholic's provocations are not directed at him personally, and that the alcoholic's difficulty in respecting himself is no reason for the caretaker to compound it by reinforcing the feeling.

When the alcoholic has just stopped drinking, or is physically ill, or is guilty and remorseful about his drinking behavior, he will openly express feelings of being no good and challenge the caretaker's therapeutic abilities to their limits. A dramatic illustration is the instance of an alcoholic seen by a psychiatrist in the emergency service of our hospital. Disheveled, unkempt, and intoxicated, the alcoholic insisted that the doctor call him "Bum." The patient was obviously perturbed when the doctor continued to address him as "Mister." When questioned, the patient elaborated convincingly and with feeling on why he ought to be called "Bum" and did not deserve to be called "Mister."

Another expression of inferiority that asks the caretaker to join in is exemplified by the "happy" drunk, who clownishly engages in amusing antics. Like the clown, he is the butt of his own jokes and poignantly reveals his hatred of himself by forswearing his dignity as a human. It is often difficult not to be amused, but to laugh at the alcoholic is to confirm him in his belief in his inner worthlessness. Just as with direct manifestations of inferiority, the therapeutic course is one of consistency and acceptance, the caretaker unbeguiled by the alcoholic's seductively provocative behavior.

In the preceding, we examined how feelings of omnipotence and worthlessness emerge from the infantile state of dependency. We observed that these feelings are probably universal, but that their domination of an individual's behavior occurs only when certain conditions, such as heightened dependency needs and their frustration, are met. This picture appears regularly in alcoholics. Inferiority and superiority feelings and their expression vary in alcoholics according to the ways in which they cope with dependency needs. The dependent alcoholic expresses feelings of inadequacy openly, though he makes strenuous attempts to justify unrealized ambitions and capabilities. The counterdependent alcoholic typically flatters himself, emphasizing his superior uniqueness. The dependent-independent shows both behaviors. Knowledge of the influence that feelings of inferiority and superiority exert on alcoholics, especially in regard to employment, is necessary to those who care for alcoholics.

7

SOCIABILITY AND RELATIONSHIPS

WE ARE gregarious and curious folk. We worry and fret about how we get along, or fail to get along, with those around us. Our worries have not passed unnoticed by social commentators, and much has been said and written about people "relating" to one another. The alcoholic, it has been noted, does not get along with others in ways that satisfy himself or the other person. This failure is best understood when we know about relationships that do satisfy both partners and when we avoid some common misconceptions about relations between people.

What are the basic criteria of a "good" or positive relationship between two people in our society? Ideally, a positive relationship is a long-term attachment between two people from which each person derives deep satisfaction, and in which mutual trust, acceptance, and dependency flourish, but conflict and anger are not strangers, and in which each party does not relinquish his integrity as an individual to the other. The capacity to form such a relationship rests upon many factors, including ease in trusting and depending on other people, and freedom in facing conflict and expressing anger. In addition, one must be aware of oneself and one's capacities, esteeming oneself in the fulfillment of these capacities, without self-denigration for what one is realistically unable to do. Mutual dependence without loss of identity permits acceptance of the economic, social, and psychological responsibilities inherent in being an adult in our society.

In positive relationships, conflicts are not long pushed into the psychological underbrush where they may eventually start a conflagration that destroys the relationship. Nor is anger so frightening to either party that it cannot be expressed. A positive relationship does not have to be as smoothly running as the Pollyannas of society would have us believe. Resolution of conflict strengthens a relationship, so does attainment of compromises where one relinquishes immediate goals for the sake of the other person. The person realizes that such sacrifices do not represent a serious infringement on his integrity as an individual. One observation recurs with sufficient frequency to merit remark. Relationships that to external appearance show frequent conflict often last a lifetime, whereas relationships that reflect the middle-class American ideal of complete absence of conflict or untoward expression of "negative" feelings like anger or criticism may collapse under stress. The frequency of divorce among middle-aged couples with grown children attests to this phenomenon.

So a positive relationship is trusting and respecting, giving and taking, conflict and resolution. Now, there are two myths about relations between persons that becloud rational inquiries into the subject—often when alcoholics are the topic of discussion.

It is often said of a person that he doesn't "relate" to others. Since the statement is patently false, except for the hypothetical situation in which an individual is totally deprived of social intercourse, what meaning is it intended to convey? When someone relates to another person in a way that isn't socially approved, then he is tagged as an unrelating individual. Not to relate is bad. The shy, the inarticulate, and the obviously frightened are said not to relate. The visible trappings of socially approved relationships are missing. Nevertheless, the person relates, bashfully, without words, or fearfully, but he relates. Sometimes persons who are inconstant, or showy, or distant are said to be unable to relate, but again they relate: fickleness, flamboyance, or coldness—all can characterize relations between people.

The second myth, a kissing cousin of the first, appears in statements that a person "relates well," or that he "relates poorly." These statements usually mean that the person who makes the judgment likes and approves of, or dislikes and disapproves of, the way in which the judged person gets along with others. They are statements of social values. Individuals in unconventional relationships, like common-law marriages, biracial marriages, or homosexual partnerships, are often labeled as relating poorly; individuals in conventional relationships are usually considered to "relate well." Both assessments have little to do with satisfactions actually derived in a relationship. Of course, any definition of interpersonal relations has to be a statement of social values, but there is no such thing as absolute goodness or badness in interpersonal relations.

My definition of a "good" or positive relationship in our society is an ideal. In practice, many gradations and variations of this aspiration for interpersonal relations occur. But to expect even a very rough approximation to ideal positive relationships among alcoholics would be highly unrealistic. As we have repeatedly seen, the alcoholic's preoccupation and conflict about dependency needs preclude his meeting a basic condition for forming positive attachments to others. Added to this are difficulties in trusting others, in respecting himself, in giving up immediate goals for the sake of greater but less immediate satisfaction, in expressing anger, and finally, in facing conflictual feelings openly. I do not mean to say that the alcoholic derives no satisfaction from others. But satisfaction with others is rarely, if ever, totally unalloyed with dissatisfaction. He seldom enjoys himself completely in intercourse with others, for in gratifying himself at one level, he must deprive himself at another. And often, in satisfying his own needs through another person, he robs that person of pleasure.

The theme of rejection is critical to precise understanding of how alcoholics get along with others. The alcoholic predicates his psychological world on anticipation and fear of being rejected. One of his basic premises in relating to others is that the original childhood trauma, rejection, is inherent and inevitable in close and potentially satisfying relationships. He is like the moth in its relation to the flame. Desperately in search of love, warmth, and tenderness, he turns toward them, expecting to be rejected. He distrusts those whom he most wishes to trust. He suspects the motives of the one he loves. He constantly puts to the test the confidence of those to whom he is attracted. He is frightened by love. To permit himself to love and be loved runs the risk of having his conception of the world destroyed. The loss of identity implicit in his fantasy is more than he can bear.

Two diametrically opposed ways of relating to others have been ascribed to alcoholics as typical of them. The first is gregariousness, and the other is seclusiveness.

I often hear a relative, friend, or caretaker say: "He's such a nice guy when he's not drinking," or "He is so much fun when he's not on a spree," and so on. And it is true. Many alcoholics are engaging companions who enjoy the company of convivial groups and who are sought after for their charm. They have a lively sense of humor and are often consummate storytellers.

The alcoholic's sociability, most often seen if he is a counter-dependent or dependent-independent alcoholic, frequently and paradoxically coexists with an inability to maintain permanent, mutually satisfying relationships with wife, parents, or friends, or is accompanied by relationships riddled with guilt, hostility, threats of rejection, and mutual recriminations. His sociability, genuine and likable as it is, rarely occurs in a deeply positive emotional relationship, but is superficial in that anyone who comes into contact with the alcoholic may be the recipient of feelings of good fellowship and camaraderie; that is, his sociability is indiscriminate. Further, as we have seen, part of his social charm represents the alcoholic's tendency to impress others with his worth, his adventures, his accomplishments in life, including well-worked-out reasons that serve to explain his failures.

Sociability in the counterdependent alcoholic is often hail-fellow-well-met, an extroverted gregariousness, sometimes apparent in small groups, sometimes in confidential tête-à-têtes. In groups, the over-all effect is strongly reminiscent of childhood play groups and of later adolescent gangs. Adult revisitation of the past is a common occurrence among men, as witness poker parties, athletic groups, and other stag, all-male affairs. But in the alcoholic, sojourns into the past become noticeable by their frequency and regularity. And, contrary to common adult practice, the identity of those in the group is not critically important; any group suffices, and individual members are expendable and replaceable. In one-to-one relationships the alcoholic may quickly establish an apparently deep and emotionally significant bond. Repeated meetings reveal to the other person, however, that the alcoholic's caring is unrelated to him as an individual but serves some other end. The relationship is betrayed when the companion hears the same stories, jokes, and confidences over and over again, presented as if they had not been told before. The sense of charm and emotional contact gradually fades as the other person realizes that he is not being seen for himself, but is serving another purpose for the alcoholic, a purpose that essentially excludes him from the relationship and leaves him with a sometimes humiliating feeling of having been psychologically used. The person has been used as a mirror in which the alcoholic sees himself reflected at his best.

Seclusiveness is hardly the same as gregariousness. Yet this, too, has been used to describe the alcoholic. The alcoholic as lone drinker is a popular conception, deriving in part from accounts such as Charles Jackson's *The Lost Weekend*. Typified by solitary behavior, the lone drinker withdraws from all relationships except the one with the bottle. He seeks psychic surcease by attempting to find, or rediscover, a primitive, infantile, nirvana-like state. Lone drinking unquestionably occurs, but it likely happens only episodically, except for the infrequent instances touched upon below. Even in classic literary accounts solitariness is not a centralizing theme. Many alcoholics drink only with others present, and many drink with others and by themselves. Drinking alone may or may not be a sign of a recluse. Since the amount the alcoholic wishes to consume exceeds acceptable standards in most social groupings, he often gets a head start on others at a party by having a couple of drinks by himself before he arrives; or at the party he will sneak drinks in the kitchen; or after the party is over, he will continue a solitary party—or he may do all three. But this solitary drinking is not necessarily seclusive. Secretive drinking does not have to be solitary drinking. Rather its function may be simply to keep others from knowing how much one is drinking.

True withdrawal from people does occur among alcoholics who are schizoid or flagrantly schizophrenic; and among these personality types, drinking is not directly related to conflict over dependency needs.

The dependent alcoholic, who openly seeks dependent gratifications in his relations with others, is prone to form long-term attachments with one person. This person may be a relative or an older man or woman. The relationship is often masochistic, since the alcoholic is seemingly willing to do anything to maintain protection and comfort. He may be obsequious, compliant, deferential, or may allow himself to be completely dominated by another person. His resentment over assuming a dependent status is only inferentially apparent, except when he is drinking. The pent-up hostility may burst forth in recriminations, biting sarcasm, or sulkiness. When he sobers up, he is contrite and seeks forgiveness.

Sometimes, however, a dependent alcoholic may develop a subtly sadistic relationship to another person, in which he is demanding, whining, and petulant. Here he seizes upon opportunities to arouse guilt in the other person, in hope of maintaining the relationship. Such comments as "If you really loved me, you wouldn't treat me this way," or "I can see you don't care for me; otherwise, you would . . . ," are the rule in such relations. The alco-

97

holic sometimes justifies the relationship by falling back on real or imagined inadequacies in himself: "You know that if I were able, I would do it, but with my heart [stomach, arthritic] condition, you really can't expect me to." A statement like this is calculated to keep the other person in line. Obviously the alcoholic's partner wouldn't stick with him unless he (or she) had needs that complement the alcoholic's. It doesn't matter whether the relationship is sadistic or masochistic. A person without strong needs either to dominate, or to be debased by, another person would not long tolerate either type of relationship.

From the caretaker's standpoint, either form of relationship has a clinginess, a sense of being enveloped and swallowed, that can be extremely disturbing, especially if the caretaker himself has not completely come to terms with his dependency needs. This reaction is sufficiently common so that dependent alcoholics should not have long-term, intensive contacts with a single caretaker; rather, their relations with individuals in any agency can be diffused in an attempt to create a sense of belongingness with the agency and not with any particular individual in it.

We know that the dependent-independent alcoholic relates to other people in both dependent and counterdependent ways. One of his interpersonal behaviors is "pigeonholing" the dependency conflict into different compartments. The alcoholic may cling masochistically to his wife, with whom he assumes his characteristically dependent style, yet he may simultaneously assume a counterdependent role with those on the job. This is virtually a double life. His wife would be amazed and unbelieving if she knew about his assertive behavior at work. Similarly, his job mates would be surprised and uncomprehending if they caught a glimpse of his clinging behavior at home. More surprising perhaps is the fact that the alcoholic himself is unaware of inconsistency in his behavior. A graphic example of this kind of relating in alcoholics may be seen in Hickey, the central figure in Eugene O'Neill's *The*

Iceman Cometh. Pigeonholing burns the candle at both ends, the alcoholic meeting dependent wishes and counterdependent needs at virtually the same time.

When evaluating an alcoholic, the caretaker should attempt to make himself familiar with his client's major modes of relating to others, so that he will be able to determine whether the alcoholic pigeonholes conflict. This knowledge is therapeutically important when phychotherapy is contemplated, since discontinuous relationships are a vulnerable chink in the alcoholic's character armor. If the therapeutic aim is the strengthening of current positive patterns of function, the caretaker may attempt to consolidate whichever mode of relating seems most effective, at the expense of that which is less effective.

In what ways do alcoholics relate to caretakers? We are particularly concerned with long-term rehabilitative situations involving social workers, pastoral counselors, psychologists, psychiatrists, and others who practice some form of psychological intervention. What can we expect to find generally with alcoholics? First, all relations with caretakers will be accompanied by the alcoholic's trepidation about direct and steady scrutiny of his inner self. This is called resistance. The caretaker must be prepared to be seduced, misled, rebuffed, challenged, and thwarted by his client. Sometimes the alcoholic's behavior seems personally directed at the caretaker. But the alcoholic merely wishes to preserve himself. When the caretaker treats him as a self-sufficient person who can operate on his own, the dependent alcoholic feels surprised, unbelieving, and distrustful. Sensing that he may have to move away from his dependent needs, he becomes more dependent than ever. The counterdependent alcoholic does it this way. He meets attempts to go beyond his sociable and affable façade with anger, resentment, avoidance, flight, and other actions designed to demonstrate how bad and incorrigible he is.

Another general characteristic is that all alcoholics are suspicious of the motives of others, especially those who respect and trust them. They do not conceive that anyone could genuinely and wholeheartedly esteem them and treat them as an equal and as an adult. They think of such a person as crazy, funny, or otherwise odd; or as a manipulator who lies to them for some purpose of his own; or as a stupid person who should know better but doesn't. Fear of trust is so great that they must find ways to denigrate and debase anyone who respects them. With genuine respect and with failure of an alcoholic's hostile maneuvers to occasion retaliatory counterattacks, the alcoholic will eventually come to accept the other person. When this occurs, we can be fairly certain that therapy will ultimately be effective, because acceptance signals a major change not simply in the alcoholic's view of others but, more significantly, in his view of himself.

What are some specific ways alcoholics relate to caretakers when embarking on a long-term therapeutic trip? One is exalting the relationship. The alcoholic says to the caretaker at the end of the first or second interview: "Oh, you're so wonderful and so helpful! I know so much about myself now that I can go on my own." This is bad news for it often signals the abrupt termination of treatment. Exalting the therapist is common among all alcoholics but happens most frequently in dependent alcoholics, who are fearful of exploring themselves, yet cannot directly and explicitly leave treatment because they fear the authority they invest in the therapist. Leaving treatment is a hostile act for them, and they fear the therapist's wrath. Exalting the therapist makes for a graceful exit. Alcoholics who feel coerced into treatment may adopt this practice: they feel that they must go along with therapy for a decent interval, so that they can at least say they were in earnest. Such abortions of treatment often herald a period of distinct improvement; improvement, however, rarely lasts for any length of time. The caretaker who allows treatment to terminate under these circumstances without taking action does a disservice to his patient now and probably in the future as well, since first encounters affect later ones. Even if it affronts his pride, the caretaker can indicate with definiteness and conviction that he appreciates the patient's flattery, but he is not that wonderful, and at this early stage nothing has been accomplished in treatment; the patient does not understand what he is doing, and he must have other reasons, not yet apparent, for wishing to leave treatment. A direct confrontation like this often strengthens a therapeutic attachment so that it continues renewed. But, even if he leaves treatment, the patient will respect the caretaker because he knows inside himself that the caretaker is right and understands him. Against this emotional backdrop he will be more able to seek treatment in the future than if nothing had been said.

Another type of relationship that alcoholics attempt to establish in treatment might be called "experts together." A typically counterdependent form of relationship, it occurs when an alcoholic identifies with a caretaker, in essence saying, let's try to understand all those others or, alternatively, let's try to understand what alcoholism is all about. It is a potentially useful relationship at the start of treatment provided that it is not permitted to continue over a long period of time. It lessens the anxiety implicit in self-scrutiny, but also bolsters the alcoholic's self-esteem by his identification with a prestigeful figure. In treatment a good deal can be done by indirection. When a patient wants to understand what alcoholism is all about, the caretaker may ask him about his thoughts, ideas, and opinions, all of which are personally relevant and meaningful, even if presented in the unemotional context of a case study. Such a relationship, continued over several meetings, allows patient and caretaker to come to know one another and to be comfortable together. Less important, but nonetheless therapeutic, the alcoholic learns about others with drinking problems, if only intellectually, and therefore deepens his perspective on himself. Ultimately, the therapeutic effect of this relationship if continued becomes less

101

and less, and the psychological distance from significant feelings greater and greater. Often, the alcoholic himself grows disenchanted with treatment and eventually stops coming. The caretaker, therefore, at some relatively early point must begin to make confrontations aimed at interrupting the process. If such questions as "How might this apply to you?" or "Have you ever felt that way yourself?" are not successful in breaking the experts-together theme, they are eventually followed up by more direct confrontations to this effect: "We've talked a good deal about people with drinking problems and about alcoholism, and this is all to the good, but I notice that you haven't spoken much of your own feelings; I know it is hard for you to do this, but that is what we're here for." Usually this is not more than the alcoholic can bear since a positive bond between caretaker and alcoholic has been established in previous meetings; and whether he expresses it or not, the alcoholic appreciates your indication that you have not been fooled by his need to avoid himself, that you understand what goes on inside him.

I once saw a man who varied the experts-together theme by making it experts-in-competition. He was bright and well-read in the psychotherapeutic literature. As he spoke about his feelings and situations that evoked them, he made his own interpretations about their deeper meaning. If I made a comment aimed at furthering self-understanding, he would compare it with his unspoken interpretation and give each of us points for the breadth, depth, and accuracy of our respective interpretations. When he told me what he was doing, I wondered with him what he was trying to prove. Besides a clear-cut difficulty in trusting me, manifested in his consciously controlling therapy, there was a feeling that, despite a lack of professional training, he was a therapist as good if not better than I, which was an immediate boost to his self-regard.

A third form of relationship, dehumanizing or depersonalizing the therapist, typically shows itself after an alcoholic has been seeing a caretaker for some time. It usually arises when the alcoholic begins to feel warm and close to the caretaker, and it serves a defensive purpose of pushing the caretaker away. Simultaneously, the alcoholic is saying, "Please be warmer to me." Dehumanizing the therapist signifies an indirect plea that the therapist take care of him in a more intimate fashion. Sometimes the alcoholic divests the caretaker of qualities of warmth and interest: "You never say anything; don't you have any feelings?" Remarks like this indicate the patient's fear of, yet desire for, a closer relationship with his therapist. Another patient will feel that the caretaker is not interested in him as an individual, but is just carrying out the job he gets paid for and has to do whether he likes it or not. This attitude enables the alcoholic to dismiss, as not serious, confrontations the caretaker makes: "You say that to all your patients." Sometimes the patient will accuse his therapist of making comments mechanically without regard for his, the patient's, own uniqueness. This perception also permits the alcoholic to run down the therapist by saying, "If you're just a technician, a blind applier of rules, then you can't be much good."

The caretaker who is aware of and understands the defensive nature of the patient's stance can easily cope with this form of resistance, for he will consistently aim at helping the alcoholic to see what feelings underlie the negative attitude. The therapist who fails to understand the process in a feeling way may get himself into difficulty by responding to the alcoholic's remarks at their face value. In distinction to exalting or identifying with the therapist, both of which flatter the caretaker (as being either wonderful or an undisputed expert), dehumanization may be seen by the therapist as an attack. Attacks are difficult to take, especially for caretakers who feel that they are cool, or unemotional, or mechanical with people. Similarly, the caretaker who is in conflict about job or career may feel that the patient who accuses him of not doing his job out of choice is correct. Patients, whether alcoholic or not, are extraordinarily clever and perceptive about those things that personally concern the therapist himself, and patients seize upon these features in the service of resistance. All remarks, thoughts, and fantasies of a patient which refer to the caretaker must be examined in light of the patient's needs and defenses and must not be taken as objective comments about the therapist's personality. Only then can the therapist view the interpersonal situation objectively, and so be in the best position to help the patient. Parenthetically, a therapist sometimes dislikes a patient. The caretaker who is unable to understand and resolve this dislike quickly should transfer the patient to another therapist. When this is impossible, it may be wiser not to see the patient for a protracted period rather than to establish what will be a false relationship.

The final type of therapeutic alliance differs from the others because it involves female caretakers only. Since most social workers are women and since social workers frequently work with alcoholics in long-term psychotherapeutic endeavors, this relationship requires discussion. A patient may sexualize his relationship to a female therapist; sexualization can range from general expressions of love and affection between a man and a woman to concrete expressions of sexual desires and wishes. While symbolizing the need to be loved and nurtured, sexualization serves to bolster the alcoholic's image as a man while avoiding the main issue: early dependent attachments to his mother. Direct avowals of love or sexual interest can disturb and frighten, or flatter, a woman therapist. Indirect expressions, such as recounting one's past sexual exploits, are less personally involving. As with other forms of relating that involve the caretaker, the woman therapist who understands what the patient's unconscious aim is and directs her attention to it avoids getting involved and is therapeutic. Obviously she does not assume postures and attitudes that might be interpreted by the patient as seductive. Except in the late stages of treatment, she does not attempt to analyze a patient's sexual feelings toward her. But she cannot ignore sexualization of the relationship, permitting it to go unchecked, for it will culminate with the alcoholic departing from treatment feeling that he has been rejected. The feelings must be dealt with therapeutically, without making technically correct, direct interpretations that are more than the patient can accept. Since expressions of love and sexual interest are, after all, ways in which the patient shows his liking for the caretaker, she can utilize these positive feelings to help him look at himself more closely by making a confrontation that includes the following points: you have spoken a lot about your feelings toward me, and yet when you look at them more closely, you really know little about me as a person; you seem to be trying to tell me something about yourself and your feelings that is difficult for you to say; I wonder what it is. As with the earlier situation of exalting the relationship (of which sexualization may be seen as a specific instance), the alcoholic is usually relieved to discover that he has not been fooling the caretaker and that she understands him.

A woman therapist I supervised treated an alcoholic poet, a man in his early thirties, divorced, and with a history of being a lady's man and of being in and out of therapy. The therapist, a warm and giving woman with a particular interest in working with artistically gifted and creative patients, showed her interest in him from the beginning. This interest, effective with lonely, withdrawn individuals, was more than sufficient to whet the poet's ardor. Within three or four interviews, it became clear that he was developing an intense positive relationship toward his therapist. In supervision, I suggested that she try to inhibit her natural interest and adopt a neutral emotional attitude during the interviews. However, along about the fifth interview the patient confessed that he was madly in love with her, that he knew nothing could come of it because of the doctor-patient relation, and that he had to stop coming to treatment because to see her and not be able to do anything about it would break his heart. He was extremely eloquent. The therapist was panic-stricken, and felt that her only recourse was to transfer him to another therapist. As we went over the situation in supervision, it appeared that the man was afraid to continue therapy for fear of what he would find and that a transfer would probably not work. I told the therapist that she could transfer him if she wished, but I suggested that she confront the patient with the fact that he could hardly be in love with her since he hardly knew her and with the idea that getting to know oneself can be a frightening prospect, with the implied question that perhaps he was afraid of therapy. She was dubious, but agreed to try it. The effect was instantaneous. The patient said that his sexual overtures toward her, as well as to other women, were brave gestures to cover feelings of sexual inadequacy. He despised women because they never saw him as other than a figure of romance and never went beyond his guise of sexuality. He felt that the therapist, the first woman to see beyond his sexual front, truly understood him.

In this chapter, I have attempted to tie together observations interspersed throughout earlier chapters about how alcoholics relate to people with a definition of ideal positive relationships between people in our society. The alcoholic by his very make-up cannot attain an ideal relationship without therapeutic assistance. The alcoholic's well-known sociability tends to be surface social charm, and the lone drinker is more myth than reality. Alcoholics develop many different relationships with caretakers in the course of long-term psychological treatment, such as exalting the therapist, developing an experts-together theme, dehumanizing the therapist, and sexualizing the relationship.

8

THE ALCOHOLIC WOMAN

FOR WOMEN in American society issues of dependency do not assume the pivotal role that they do for men. This has little, perhaps nothing, to do with basic drives, but is the product of society's tolerant attitude toward dependent behavior on the distaff side. Biologically rooted needs for immediate and unconditional nurture and body contact do not differ between the sexes, but cultural postures about expressing these needs are typified by a sharp sexual cleavage. This has distinct implications for personality development in boys and girls in our society. In an earlier chapter we saw that American boys are alienated from the biological push of dependency at an early age; after infancy and toddlerhood, they are permitted few opportunities to engage in dependent activities. The societal emphasis centers on independence, self-reliance, holding off expressions of feeling, and individuality. The repression of desires to be dependent has profound implications for personality organization in adulthood. Alcoholic men adopt one of three methods of coping with buried dependency needs—methods common enough in the general populace but seen in exaggerated and distorted form among alcoholics.

The natural history of the way in which women cope with dependent needs is relatively unhampered by cultural restrictions. To this degree, the development of women vis-à-vis dependency is direct, uncomplicated, and possesses a certain organic naturalness. Dependent behavior among women is not frowned upon in our society. Reliance on others, seeking aid and comfort, expressing one's sentimental needs, and similar characteristics are generally considered to be typically feminine. There is certainly no thought that this is untoward behavior; their integration into our culturally bound concept of femininity is so complete that, far from occasioning comment, these characteristics are hardly noticed.

What happens in a girl whose parents frustrate her needs to be cared for unconditionally? As with boys, frustrating a girl has the effect of increasing the intensity of a need, making it stronger than before. It is as if frustration were a dam which blocks the flow of a need, so that the need grows larger and larger; there must be a sluiceway to release increasing pressure. For the girl in our society the sluiceway is the more readily available because she faces no cultural barrier that coincides with, and thereby strengthens, the frustration she experiences within her family. And so a girl raised in a milieu that frustrates dependency often grows up to be an openly dependent person.

The alcoholic woman often falls into the openly dependent category of the triumvirate described for male alcoholics. More frequently than with men, her dependent overtures are accompanied by an aggressive insistence that her needs be fulfilled. She does not apologize for her requests; the obsequiousness and deference typifying the openly dependent alcoholic man are usually not apparent in the alcoholic woman. She sees no reason to apologize for what is, after all, her cultural birthright. But there is every reason to insist and demand that her needs be met because of that same birthright. The alcoholic woman feels that she has been left out, that she is missing something justifiably hers. The man, on the other hand, senses something "wrong" in dependence and so apologizes, or comes seeking love like a whipped dog who expects to be whipped again. The alcoholic woman with central conflicts over dependency is proud, even arrogant, in her demands, whereas the openly dependent man is often overly apologetic and overly humble. When demands are gratified, the woman gives no thanks; the man can't thank you enough.

The observation that open dependency is characteristic of alcoholic women may in part explain why they follow treatment recommendations and stay in treatment longer than their male counterparts. As we know, the openly dependent alcoholic is quite ready to engage upon a course of treatment, especially when he sees in it possibilities of being taken care of. Those who care for the woman alcoholic must be warned, however, to expect possibly disconcerting behaviors. If she is openly dependent, she may be unrelenting in her demands: fulfillment only gradually diminishes the frequency with which they are made. Furthermore, the helping person who likes visible evidence that efforts in a client's behalf are appreciated is apt to be sorely disappointed when his client is a woman with alcohol problems.

A colleague of mine saw a woman alcoholic for many years. While her problem with alcohol was complicated by other factors in her personality and in her life, the dominating impression upon meeting her was that she took it for granted that she could rely on you. Over the years she showed great improvement, interspersed with major slips during which she would disappear for weeks on end. During these bouts she called her therapist regularly and, after they were over, would return to therapy unannounced, but at her usual time. If the therapist had, in her absence, scheduled "her hour" for someone else, she became extremely angry.

This woman's open dependency characterizes many female alcoholics, but few male alcoholics, even when they belong in the openly dependent category. The quality of her dependency differs because it is directly expressed, taken for granted, and unaccompanied by guilt. Her relatively nonconflictual readiness to rely on others is an advantage in treatment since it means that therapy is not prematurely terminated, as so often occurs with men whose conflicts over dependency lead to guilt or accusations that the caretaker is harmful rather than helpful—and this even in openly dependent alcoholics who still have remnants of unresolved dependency conflict.

The absence of cultural constraints against women expressing dependency sometimes results in extreme and undisguised manifestations of dependency, as happened in the case of an alcoholic professional woman I once knew. She was divorced and had two small children. Her drinking had little noticeable effect on her work, and she earned enough to have a nursemaid during the day for her children. After five years of this arrangement she decided it was too exhausting to come home after work and take care of the children. Without advance preparation, she gave up her job and traveled unannounced to the distant home of her recently widowed mother-in-law, an elderly lady who lived alone, had suffered much personal misfortune, and was rather masochistic. Although uninvited, she remained dependent on her mother-in-law for four months while she made ineffectual attempts to obtain work and make arrangements for the care of her children. The mother-in-law, out of a sense of duty to her grandchildren that conspired with her masochism, made the feeblest of protests about the situation. It is instructive to note that during this period in which the alcoholic's dependency needs were gratified, she drank not at all.

Despite its prominence in women, use of dependency as an organizing focus to explore personality structure is not as satisfactory for women as for men alcoholics. Dependency occupies a place secondary to the central dilemma for women in twentieth-century American society. For the first time in history women in large numbers have the time, ability, and education to occupy roles and positions never before occupied by them, yet there are powerful social and cultural forces which, while gradually and slowly disintegrating, block access to these positions. Through their teens and early twenties girls are now trained to expect that they will occupy, and complete their sense of adequacy in, positions of traditionally masculine responsibility. Only after college or, now, often graduate school, and the usually vain search for a career, and the turn back to the traditional role of *Küche, Kinder,* and *Kirche,* does the woman begin to feel that she has been the victim of a grand hoax. It is at the point of completion of college or just prior to marriage that I often see in my practice young women of undoubted accomplishments and achievements suddenly beset by feelings of personal inadequacy that are completely at variance with what they have actually done. The feelings they convey are that they have been promised something and it has not been forthcoming, that they are missing some indefinable thing that they were supposed to get, that they are impotent to do the things they want to do, and that they do worse than poorly in the activities they do engage in. The idea of the unfulfilled promise and the despairing sense of ineptness go hand in hand.

Women in this position may turn to any one of a variety of solaces. Most bury themselves, often with a vengeance, in the traditional role of housewife, sometimes spiced by participation in social and community affairs. A few reach the promised land. And here the stereotype of the hypermasculine professional woman is, like that of the plain, earnest, and bespectacled Radcliffe student, rapidly being shattered. More and more I see in career women, especially those with families, a flexibility, a liveliness, and a sense of inner comfort and worth, that makes those for whom the promise remains unfulfilled all the more poignant. Then there are those who seek the answer from sexuality, from drugs, and finally from alcohol.

The intelligent, educated, ambitious woman who takes refuge in domesticity, forgoing yet promising herself that "someday" she'll get back to an embryonic career, is particular prey to depression during her middle years. Buoyed by the promise of youth and the early joys of marriage, immersed in the hectic activity of child, home, and husband care, she finds the years pass quickly by. Then in her middle forties, when youth and feminine beauty are fast fading, with a husband increasingly involved in work or in recapturing his own youth, and children leaving home for school or for marriage, the promise seems impossible to obtain. Familiar and comfortable supports withdrawn, she comes to feel that the past twenty years were perhaps not what she wanted after all, but that it is now too late. Feelings of futility and an empty future beset her. During this dangerous period in her life new, more trustworthy friends may be sought. And alcohol may be one of them.

Another time of personal peril occurs when the children are small, requiring constant attention. The vigilance without thought —and preventing thought—that the situation requires can be so frustrating that she may turn to sherry or a highball to relax taut nerves. For this natural release of tension to eventuate in unhealthy use of alcohol requires that her psychological development be stunted so that she has only limited inner resources to combat frustration and anxiety.

The central, perhaps inevitable, feature in women with alcoholic problems is a concern, even a preoccupation, about being inadequate and inept, surrounded by an aura of futility that bespeaks her utter helplessness to change herself. The profound conviction of her inadequacy is one aspect of this complex that is diamond-hard in its indestructability. Obviously, depression is often the dominant and complicating emotional accompaniment. The principal task of treatment with the alcoholic woman is to change this fixed image of herself. And this is always a slow and gradual process.

Drinking is often justified on the basis of inadequacy and its presumed unchangeability. "I am such an awful person that I might as well act like one" is a common justification. Alternatively, when she must exonerate herself, "The world is such an awful place, I might as well drown it out." It has been said that female alcoholics more frequently drink to insensibility than male alcoholics. The truth of the statement is uncertain, but there is some plausibility in the notion that the woman drinks to recapture a sense of worth she had before she realized the promise would not be fulfilled.

Recently, I saw a woman whose severe problem with alcohol had started only two years previously. Her history belied her current condition, for it sounded like the American dream come true. She had graduated from high school at the top of her class and had been one of the most popular girls in it; at college she was equally popular. Upon graduation, again near the top of her class and a promising artist, she married a highly eligible classmate, a young man expected to go places. He lived up to all expectations; they had three lovely children, a beautiful home, and all the amenities. There was never a shadow of dissension in the family, and their children, bright and interested, appeared to be following in the parental footsteps. Then, without warning, their eldest son, a freshman in college, quit school, saying he was going to travel about the country using his own resources. When his dismayed parents tried to understand with him what was going on and to reason with him, he suddenly blew up, saying that they had never given him anything—they had not allowed him his individuality, nor had they prepared him for adulthood. With this he disappeared for several weeks. He returned, changed in dress and appearance, to ask for some money. This situation, which continued for many months, resulted in the father angrily refusing to have anything to do with his son. The mother, who in her married life had had little experience with anger, felt responsible for her son's situation and guilty about it; she further felt she had let her now-angry husband down and was anxious for the future of her other two children.

Around this time she began to add a cocktail or two to her regular before-dinner drink. When her husband was not home (and during the recurrent crises over the son's behavior he found it ever more convenient to stay late at work), she would often drink through dinner and until he returned. Her other children told their father of her unusual behavior, but he minimized it. Within six months the problem had progressed so rapidly that he could not deny its presence but felt helpless to cope with it. A year and a half later, following hospitalization for an ankle fractured in a fall while she was drinking, she was seen by a social worker who referred her to me.

During her visits to me, it was gradually revealed that she had made an unconscious pact with her husband that she would be an excellent and dutiful wife and mother as long as the romantic aura of the ideal married couple never altered: there must be no hint of friction; all must be sweetness and light. This pact was highly suitable to her husband, a narcissistic man who liked his needs met efficiently and who himself was afraid of anger. That their son was affected by the emotional unreality of his upbringing is hardly surprising. His abrupt departure from school, his angry outburst, and the father's consequent anger at mother and child abrogated the terms of the pact for both husband and wife. It was then that the family began to crumble.

The woman, on her side, had made the pact because, as she saw it, she required restitution for losing through marriage the opportunity to realize her artistic talents. Treatment consisted in resuscitating her fast-failing sense of personal worth by repeatedly showing her that her life as wife and mother had not been wasted, by reviving her dormant artistic gifts, by helping her accept her guilt about her son and her shame about drinking, and by creating an atmosphere where she could express and examine her disused anger. Her energy and deep desire to help herself resulted in an outcome to therapy whereby she reinstated the matrimonial pact with two additions: anger is all right, and a career can be part of marriage. Her husband, by the way, was also treated, with the goal of diminishing his tendency toward angry withdrawal when his desires were blocked.

Fairly reliable evidence shows that female alcoholics often begin to drink in response to major personal crises that have in common a factor of loss. These include divorce, death, illness, and so on. How does this knowledge about events that trigger off excessive drinking coincide with our formulation of the unfulfilled promise? A woman who considers herself an inept person, who exists in an inner web of inadequacy, is prone to respond to personal tragedies involving loss in two ways. First, her sense of worthlessness makes her a ready victim of self-blame for the loss. If she had done such-and-such, her husband would not have divorced her; if she had taken better care of Jack, he would not have died; and so on. Second, what sense of worth she has is vicariously obtained from her perception of the adequacy of her loved ones and from her efforts to please them. In this sense she is extremely dependent. But the loss of a loved one leaves her feeling guilty and strips her of the vestiges of adequacy. Under these mental circumstances the onset of alcoholism, depression, or other symptomatology is not surprising.

A woman, unsure of her femininity, suffered three miscarriages, the last occurring late in pregnancy. Previously a mild social drinker, she now began to drink heavily, and became more and more flirtatious and seductive, assuming the role of a helpless girl who looked to the strong man for strength and security. Her flirtations graduated to affairs and finally to promiscuity. In treatment, she revealed that this was her way of trying to reassure herself of her femininity, to make up for her inability to have children, and to cope with depression subsequent to the loss of her never-born children.

This patient's promiscuity brings to the fore the popular notion that alcohol problems and promiscuity go together. While this may be so in individual instances, as above, the general aspect of sexuality in female alcoholics is inhibition rather than expression. And when it is expressed, sexual activity is less pleasurable than it is symptomatic of profound distress and disturbance of feelings about onself and one's sexual role. Investigations repeatedly reveal that sexual inhibition is a common factor in alcoholic women. They find sexual relations frightening, uncomfortable, and painful; sexual activity is minimal, sometimes nonexistent. Frigidity and unresponsiveness replace warmth and participation.

Among women alcoholics there is little of the bonhomie and gregarious but superficial sociability that characterizes male alcoholics. This is understandable, since the comradeship of alcoholics is confined to the counterdependent group, and we see few counterdependent alcoholics among women. There is, however, a proportionally small number of alcoholic women who drink and otherwise act like counterdependent male alcoholics. These women are not necessarily counterdependent; they have not adopted defensive but misleading postures against the insistence of their wishes to be dependent. I doubt that they are counterdependent at all in this sense; they are, rather, attempting to resolve an underlying sexual problem. They have turned away from femininity in an attempt to establish a masculine identity. They include women who drink like men at bars, who try to live up to their claim that they can drink as well as a man, and who assume the sociability of the cordial fraternity of male drinkers.

I once treated a woman whose bearing, dress, and general outlook on life were distinctly masculine. All her companions were men, and with them she belittled and derided the more feminine members of her own sex, but in the presence of women she was shy and inarticulate. She was referred to me by a physician who saw her for liver trouble associated with heavy drinking. Unlike most women alcoholics, she had begun drinking in her teens away from home, and she had been intoxicated many times before she was legally old enough to buy liquor. She was in her late thirties when I first saw her and was frightened by the ominous reality of her liver disease, as well as by the prospect of renouncing liquor. With gusto she related anecdotes of drinking parties and barroom affrays, and of helping young fellows still wet behind the ears. Interestingly, her few sexual liaisons had taken place with men, but they sounded more like primitive struggles for supremacy and survival than sexual encounters.

As I became acquainted with her and her early life, it became clear that her masculine attitude, by now a fixed part of her character, was her way of coping with feelings of helplessness. Her mother, a passive, unresisting woman and the patient's model of femininity, had been brutalized by the patient's father, an aggressive, domineering man who himself had a drinking problem. Nor had the patient escaped his punitiveness. Out of self-defense, as it were, the patient had identified with her father to an extent that buried her relation to her mother. In therapy, I attempted to stay within her personal frame of reference; she gave up drinking, but not her friends nor the bar. She gained more respect from her cronies for being able to stay away from whiskey than she had for being able to drink them under the table.

This case illustrates a major way in which women alcoholics differ from men. Typically, women do not have the lifelong, ambivalent relationship to alcohol that is characteristic of men. For men, alcohol is both deeply loved and violently hated; cultural definitions of alcohol and man's relation to it assume a significance and reality far beyond its purely physical effect on the body. Women escape this. For them, alcohol is not endowed with mystical properties. They use it like a medicine to narcotize thinking and feeling in times of pain and distress. This is one reason why women alcoholics usually begin to drink at later ages than male alcoholics, and why the beginning of drinking as a problem occurs later in life and in response to a specific crisis. The exception to this generality about female alcoholics may be seen in the "masculine drinker": when a woman identifies with a father who embodies the common masculine ambivalence toward alcohol, her attitude toward it will be characterized by a similar ambivalence.

117

The difference in the way social definitions of alcohol apply to women and to men plays a part in the lesser prevalence of alcoholism among women than among men. Not only is it more traditionally acceptable for men to drink in the first place, but alcohol is imbued with magical qualities for men, whereas for women alcohol has only its pharmacological effects. The fascination and allure of alcohol is muted for women, but blares forth for men. Little wonder that more men than women are drawn to it in ways that are ultimately harmful.

It has been said that alcoholic women are "sicker" psychologically than alcoholic men. A descriptive study undertaken over a quarter of a century ago reported that female alcoholics were seriously disturbed. The women under study were inmates in the psychiatric ward of a large municipal hospital, and their alcoholic problems were accompanied by mental disorders. If we compared these women with male alcoholics admitted to the same facility, we would find little difference between the sexes in regard to severity of pathology. The depth and breadth of disturbance in female alcoholics is probably no greater than that in men and is probably just as variable. Nevertheless, many argue otherwise. They correctly state that drunkenness and alcoholism among women are socially disapproved, but are tolerated and condoned in men. These commentators then conclude that a woman who becomes alcoholic must be very disturbed, because she flies in the face of rigid social conventions and runs the risk of social ostracism. This conclusion neglects the factor of how social values influence our perception of others. When we say that an alcoholic woman is "sicker" than an alcoholic man, we may in effect be saying she is a "worse" person because she has had the temerity to violate a cherished social ideal of femininity.

One aspect of the "sicker-than-men" point of view is the statement that more female than male alcoholics attempt and accomplish suicide. I have read the statement in several places but have never been able to track down its origin for a reference is never given to indicate its source. While studies that deal with sex difference in attempted and successful suicides among alcoholics are not entirely satisfactory, they do reveal that more men than women alcoholics attempt and actually do commit suicide.

And so much has been said of women alcoholics, little of it established fact. Relative to men, it has been said that female alcoholics are psychologically "sicker," more difficult to treat, and more variable with regard to personality structure; that female alcoholics develop the problem in a shorter span of time, attempt and accomplish suicide more often, and more frequently have an alcoholic in their family background. In addition it has been said that their drinking problems more often follow distinctly discernible personal tragedies than is the case with men, e.g., death, divorce, or other separations. Women alcoholics supposedly have more sexual problems. And, finally, there is the avowal that the gap between the number of male and female alcoholics is rapidly narrowing, or that it no longer exists.

None of these comparative "facts" are of much use in understanding and helping a woman alcoholic. More important than these isolated bits of dubious information is our attempt to see how each patient has come to grips with the social discontinuities that face women in contemporary society, what meaning losses bear to the onset of drinking, and, finally, the role dependency plays. One has to pinpoint the nature and origin of the psychic pain against which alcohol has become the self-prescribed medicine. The general case is the sense of personal inadequacy and lack of self-realization that comes with awareness that the promise of youth is not to be fulfilled in adulthood. But, as case examples illustrate, the specific forms of this general malady vary from person to person.

119

9

OUR RESPONSE TO ALCOHOLICS

"In fact, untouchables perform a priestly function in taking on themselves all human vileness."
—William S. Burroughs in *Naked Lunch*

LIKE ALL VICTIMS of persistent and widespread prejudice, alcoholics carry burdens other than their own. Along with the mentally ill, the racially different, and the nonconforming, they are the social safety valves that permit steam generated by an often inconsistent society to escape along insulated routes—while relieving society, they do not endanger it. The alcoholic suffers from an illness and suffers greatly. Why should he also be afflicted by a social disease not of his own making. Does he have to be a societal pariah? Is the picture changing? Is it possible for each of us as individuals to view the alcoholic rationally?

Some believe that increased public awareness and tolerance of emotional factors in human behavior have fostered an ever more enlightened attitude toward alcoholism. This enlightenment has been likened to changes in popular attitudes toward tuberculosis, a disease stigmatized in the early twentieth century, but now accepted as a bona fide illness without moral overtones. Punitive, moralistic, and derisive attitudes and acts toward alcoholics are said to be

120

declining, and respect and understanding and seeing alcoholism as an unasked-for health problem rather than a moral affliction are said to be on the rise. These conclusions are sometimes presented to encourage belief in a dramatic and revolutionary shift, in the dawning of a New Day. Work done in the past decade shows that no such shift has occurred. This is not to say that there has been *no* movement from negative to positive feelings about alcoholics. There are important recent developments. In the past two years the federal government, along with groups in the civil rights movement, has taken steps to ameliorate the alcoholic's plight.

The federal government's concern stems from its recognition that alcoholism is the fourth-largest public health problem in the nation, surpassed only by mental illness, heart disease, and cancer. This recognition has resulted in the establishment of a national advisory board on alcoholism as well as a national center to study ways of treating and preventing further social casualties from alcoholism.

The source of concern among civil rights workers is the abrogation of the alcoholic's constitutionally guaranteed civil liberties when he is jailed. They argue that to incarcerate a person for a manifestation of an illness is a violation of his personal freedom; since alcoholism is an illness, the civil liberty of an alcoholic is violated when he is arrested and jailed. Two court decisions to this effect mean that a person cannot be imprisoned for public intoxication or disorderly behavior if either is the result of an alcoholic illness. We would never consider an epileptic who has a seizure in public and collapses on the street a public nuisance; to arrest him would be absurd. But this is exactly what we do when an alcoholic passes out on the street! (Ironically, diabetics in coma and epileptics who have had a seizure in public *have* been arrested for drunkenness. Imagine the embarrassment, to say nothing of the anxiety about the possibility of a suit for false arrest, upon discovery of the error.)

These two developments—the increasing role of the federal government and recent court decisions—augur well for the care and treatment of alcoholics, one aspect being a shift toward more accepting public and professional attitudes. The dramatic, overnight switch of feelings is pie-in-the-sky thinking. Changes in attitudes come about slowly and usually proceed from other, sometimes completely unrelated, social changes. Only when the magnitude of social and political events warrant it is attitude change relatively rapid.

What does the literature about public and professional attitudes toward alcoholics tell us? One group of public surveys reveals an apparently high acceptance of alcoholics as persons with an illness. The late E. M. Jellinek, however, questioned the depth of this acceptance. Findings of an intensive examination of attitudes of Iowans toward alcoholics suggests that shifts in attitudes are at best slow. This investigation involved many years work surveying representative Iowans' drinking practices, attitudes toward drinking, and, most pertinent to our interests, perceptions of alcoholics and alcoholism. It was found that only fourteen percent of adults in Iowa accept alcoholics in the same spirit that they would persons with a "real" disease. Only this small proportion of people thinks that the alcoholic would be wise to talk his problem over with his family and should seek out professional aid. Over three-quarters of those surveyed either denied that the alcoholic is a sick person or found him to be "morally weak" or "weak-willed" in addition to being sick.

This particular investigation, as well as a few others, examined the feelings of the public at large. Most investigations of attitudes toward alcoholism and its victims have been restricted to doctors, psychiatrists, and other professionals, presumably because they are the ones most apt to enter into a helping role with alcoholics. If they share the punitive and hostile feelings common in the general public, and if they act upon these attitudes in their en-

122

counters with alcoholics, the alcoholic gets short shrift when he approaches the traditional dispensers of healing, help, and care in our society.

In general, the findings of these studies are discouraging, for they show that the caretaking professions have little liking for the alcoholic or understanding of him. Indeed, Robert Straus suggested that the general public has shown more rapid acceptance of alcoholism as an illness than has the medical profession, including psychiatrists and hospital administrators. Another observer wrote that social workers have avoided working with alcoholics because they see them as either "too difficult or too hopeless to help." Another student of the field indicts all professions in stating that "ignorant, moralistic, and punitive" attitudes "thrive" among caretaking professions; about the alcoholic he says: "Society despises him; the medical profession shuns him." Yet another investigator, who studied the opinions of college students and people working in a mental hospital about the mentally ill, the physically handicapped, and the alcoholic, reported that both students and hospital employees were more accepting of the physically handicapped than they were of either the alcoholic or the mentally ill. Summaries of such studies and commentary could go on and on. Their import is invariably the same: alcoholics are viewed as "weak-willed," "nuisances," or "uncooperative," and without hope as far as rehabiliation is concerned.

Does the caretaker act on these discouraged and discouraging feelings? Anecdote tells us that he does. But few scientific studies show a relation between attitude and action. A few years ago, I took part in a study that came about fortuitously as an accidental offshoot of a treatment project upon which we were engaged. It came about this way. We were selecting alcoholic patients for the project from the emergency service of our hospital and knew, from other investigations, the numbers of patients we could expect within a given period of time. When we became aware that patients were being referred at about half the anticipated rate, we decided, partly out of curiosity and partly because the slowdown was holding us up, to find out what was going on.

Fortunately, information was available to enable us to determine the precise nature of the blockage of patient flow. Doctors in the emergency service had been asked to refer any patient whom they diagnosed as alcoholic. As it turned out, they referred roughly half of the patients who could have been diagnosed as alcoholic. The other half they failed to refer, but dealt with in other ways. When we compared characteristics of referred alcoholics to those of nonreferred, we found two things: first, missed cases were more socially intact than referred patients, and, second, they suffered from more obvious, clear-cut, and traditional medical problems than referred alcoholics. Men that were referred possessed most of the signs that identify the socially deteriorated and impoverished skid-row alcoholic.

As two distinct images came into focus, one of a socially intact but physically ill person, the other of a relatively physically well but *déclassé* individual, we began to guess the enormous role that attitudes of the referring doctors were playing in the decision to refer patients to us. We speculated first that physicians have a skid-row stereotype of the alcoholic and that a person must live up to this stereotype before he will be diagnosed as alcoholic—this despite the fact that skid-row alcoholics comprise no more than 5 percent of all alcoholics. Second, when signs and symptoms of alcoholism are present in a person who appears socially intact, the doctor is loath to make the diagnosis. Third, when traditional medical conditions accompany or complicate an alcoholic condition, the "respectable" problem is treated to the exclusion of the alcoholic disorder. In order to tie down these speculations we interviewed the referring doctors about their feelings toward alcoholism, alcoholics, and referring alcoholics to our project. Our speculations were definitely, but not unequivocally, supported by the information from these interviews.

124

That doctors see alcoholism as a disorder of derelicts is indicated in this remark, not unrepresentative, of one doctor: "In the emergency ward, somebody comes in and it's pretty much of a snap judgment. If he looks like an alcoholic, smells like an alcoholic, is pretty much of a degenerate as far as his appearance—disheveled, filthy, dirty—hasn't been holding down a job, you draw an immediate impression on this basis." Or, from another doctor: "People whom I have considered alcoholic, all the time . . . that I was there, have never been properly dressed. They have all been dirty, although there were one or two exceptions." And, again: "We see a lot of derelict and bum-type alcoholics. . . . We just get sort of used to the old sort of Bowery-type individual in the emergency ward." In these and other comments the doctors reveal that for them alcoholism is a disorder of derelicts. They also show in their comments that the alcoholic-as-derelict represents only one type of alcoholism. For example, the first doctor quoted above completed his statement by remarking: "This certainly doesn't distinguish the well-dressed executive who comes in, who may be just as much of an alcoholic as the average person who gets to the emergency ward." Nevertheless, our findings about referred and missed cases show that the doctor acts upon the feeling that alcoholics are derelicts.

The doctor's hesitancy in diagnosing alcoholism in a socially intact person is all too clear in the following comment: "Are you going to consider, for instance, a fellow who is vice-president of the local bank, who consumes a good fifth of the best every day after lunch to dinner time, and yet eats a good dinner and carries on his business activities perfectly well, an alcoholic? I don't know." Deference to scruples like these is one not insignificant reason why some alcoholics find it desperately difficult to get treatment. A second doctor adopts a similar point of view: "I've known people who've had relatives in their homes who were alcoholics for years, but they weren't aware of it for a long time. I would call that type of individual a problem drinker, but I wouldn't label him an alcoholic until I knew the specific circumstances of his situation."

The self-reassuring reliance on a diseased body-part, rather than dealing with a person, stands out in these remarks: "All the subtle things in life, the implied things, people's sensitive problems, just go right by the resident. He's interested in hemorrhage, pain and so forth." Or: "The pressure is on other patients. For example, somebody is there with a leg injury, which is definitely obvious. We have more sympathy toward him than with this person who is only drunk." It should be noted that the frequency of death among alcoholics in delirium tremens is high from a medical vantage point. And, finally: "One of the main problems that the resident down here has is to see just medical, honest, medical-surgical problems, without the alcoholic who comes in and wants a place to sleep."

I do not wish to leave the reader with a picture of doctors as thoughtless and cruel. The doctors we interviewed are intelligent, articulate, interested, and aware, and I have selected certain of their comments to make particular points about some of their conceptions of alcoholics. Not all doctors are blind to their attitudinal shortcomings, nor do they fail to struggle against expressing their thoughts in action. One doctor put it this way: "We should not show any partiality to the person who has the leg injury, as compared to the person who is just plain out because of alcoholism. They are both patients. One has a different type of problem from the other." Another said: "If the practice of medicine is invariably related to somatic complaints, well then, I don't see how you can expect to practice in an emergency service." Or elsewhere, I might add.

This study is one of the few systematic inquiries into doctors' attitudes toward alcoholics that relates attitudes to the doctor's behavior. The implications of the doctor's differential actions are better understood in light of the fact that referral to the project

126

meant that a patient received comprehensive care for alcoholism and its medical, social, and psychological complications. The doctor was referring the alcoholic to a treatment program for alcoholics with an ideal therapeutic philosophy. When a doctor failed to refer a patient, he did the patient a disservice. The irony of this pattern of referral is that alcoholics most likely to benefit from the program were the ones least likely to be sent to it. The socially deteriorated alcoholic who subsists in the unstable skid-row millieu has always been known as the most challenging, but unrewarding, candidate for any of the known therapies of alcoholism, whereas the more socially intact alcoholic, who has far more to lose in terms of family, job, and community standing, is much more responsive to treatment. Alcoholics, it appears, are blocked from getting into treatment by the very caretaking apparatus designed for their benefit.

Many times I have seen patients from professional or business backgrounds who have been in and out of hospitals for years with nutritional disturbances, liver damage, or polyneuropathies without a diagnosis of alcoholism being made and only the physical condition treated. And often I have heard of well-to-do patients admitted to the private wings of hospitals with the intention of "drying out," or as it is now called, "detoxification," but with an "acceptable" medical diagnosis so as not to offend the sensibilities of family, friends, and society.

Publicly supported outpatient alcoholism facilities are being established in more and more states, but tend to draw as their clientele groups of alcoholics most difficult to treat on an outpatient basis. In the meantime society conspires to hide and keep from treatment those most likely to benefit from it. The situation is even worse in regard to identifying and helping incipient and early alcoholics, although beginning studies are being made in this direction.

We have seen that attitudes about alcoholism and alcoholics

are largely denigrating and lead to actions deleterious to the alcoholic's well-being. Signs that these basic and pervasive feelings and actions are changing for the better do not signify a metamorphosis of either the rapidity or depth that some incautious optimists suggest. A question that remains unanswered is why people dislike and deride and hide alcoholics.

Sociologists, psychologists, and others have attempted to understand the nature of bias and prejudice. The irrational feelings held toward alcoholics are a special instance of prejudice. A common explanation is scapegoating, which occurs when an individual or group stands out as separate from society at large because of obvious physical, social, or other differences. The process through which differences are transmuted into "bad" characteristics is obscure, but once it has taken place society feels free to pile its morally reprehensible baggage onto the out-group, and then punishes its own shortcomings without hurting itself.

Another sociological explanation is the "safety-valve" theory referred to earlier, in which groups that can be defined and isolated from the majority on the basis of physical or behavioral distinctiveness become pariah groups that express society's illnesses, while simultaneously relieving its tensions. In our society with its increasing emphasis on defensive conformity and consensual solidarity, these safety valves are numerous and include the racially different, the mentally ill, the nonconformist, as well as the alcoholic. Our culture's inability to integrate the deviants it produces contrasts with other societies where special functions and roles give deviance its place—sometimes an honored one—in society and permit the deviant to "belong." Mystic functionaries—such as the shaman or witch doctor—are often chosen from those who obviously do not fit into the larger society; in our history, court jesters were dwarves, and until recently carnival sideshows served as socially integrated repositories for the physically abnormal.

Another way of understanding feelings about alcoholics is to examine the expectations that doctors, nurses, or social workers have about patients. Caretakers expect a patient to suffer from his ailment, to defer to the authority and expertness of the professional, to comply with treatment recommendations, and to assume that the caretaker can take action which will relieve the patient's distress. That these expectations are often frustrated by alcoholics—and other kinds of patients—is hardly new. The alcoholic seemingly "enjoys" his illness. He often violates the doctor's authority by diagnosing and prescribing for himself, as did the patient who came into a hospital clinic saying: "Give me paraldehyde; I've got D.T.'s." Doctors often feel they have little to contribute to treating the alcoholic and that this little is diminished further because the patient has control over the "etiologic agent," i.e., alcohol, by means of his "will power." The alcoholic can undermine the professional's position, until anger and resentment attendant upon frustration become apparent in the caretaker's words and actions. Unfortunately, education in many helping professions fails to prepare its future practitioners for contingencies which, when properly handled, can result in therapeutic efficacy and success.

Each view summarized plays its part in helping to explain feelings and attitudes commonly aroused in us by alcoholics. Two elements run throughout these views, elements basic to complete understanding: anxiety and guilt. The alcoholic himself does not frighten us. But our perception of him does—for this perception stimulates and awakens wishes that slumber deep within us. The intensity of unacceptable needs sets in motion processes that inevitably result in anxiety and guilt. We each have idiosyncratic ways of coping with anxiety and guilt that serve to protect us from immediate, direct experiences of them. One common way of handling anxious or guilty feelings is to attribute their cause to someone else. It is easier to be afraid of another person who can be attacked, avoided, or placated than to be afraid of oneself. In like vein, when another assumes our guilt we become blameless, while the guilty person gains either our pity and forgiveness or our censure and accusations.

The nature of forces released in us by our perception of the alcoholic has to do with the fact that he symbolizes these forces. He has lost his self-control; he is dependent; he is irresponsible— all because he drinks a substance over which we feel he should have utmost conscious control. Independence, autonomy, self-reliance, self-control, and assumption of responsibility are, as we have seen, highly valued in American society. Living up to these ideals, however, requires sacrifices: desires to be dependent, to lose control, and to be irresponsible are driven underground, and whatever threatens to bring them to light is dangerous. Because we both love and hate alcohol, we go to great lengths to see its effects as harmless fun. Irresponsible behavior or loss of self-control attendant upon becoming drunk is not only condoned, but accepted. Who has not heard, "He couldn't help it; he was drunk"? The use of alcohol has been judged to be an extenuating circumstance for a crime.

At some point, however, the use of alcohol ceases to be an excuse for irresponsibility, but becomes a mark of it. This point probably has something to do with the "willfulness" of drinking that results in loss of self-control and with repeated violation of cherished values, such as social strictures against abuse of mothers and children. When drinking repeatedly leads to dependency, loss of control, and irresponsibility, it arouses latent wishes to indulge in such behavior.

Our perception of the alcoholic as a willful miscreant who has lost his capacity to control his actions rouses within us similar wishes. The threatened eruption of these wishes into consciousness results in anxiety and guilt. We tend then among other things to attribute *all* of these dangerous wishes to the alcoholic, thus enabling us to handle our anxiety and guilt in external ways. And so we attack the alcoholic or run away from him.

The alcoholic himself is not insensible to these processes, and he intuitively grasps their significance. He is no less a member of our culture than we are and has learned his lessons equally well. He is an expert on the attitudes society reserves for those who lose themselves in drink. He punishes and tortures himself with this knowledge, but he also uses it to elicit reactions he has learned that alcoholics must expect. He reinforces and entrenches society's attitudes toward him, and this provides him with one justification for continuing his lonely, abused existence. His interest in remaining alcoholic leads him to do whatever he can to reduce or defeat inner forces that aspire to health. To be treated with respect, kindness, sympathy, and love is a hazard to his image of being unloved and unlovable, and on such occasions he redoubles efforts to prove that society is right about alcoholics. Society for its part is only too ready to let him prove his point.

The alcoholic's provocation is one thing, and our feeling about him another. This is a distinction we cannot overlook, for it is easy to rationalize our feeling, attitude, and action toward him on the ground that he is getting exactly what he asked for. Dialogue with the alcoholic is more complicated than a simple matter of action-reaction. If the alcoholic provokes us, we undoubtedly provoke him. I once saw a patron in a bar lead on a drunken man, who was trying to make everyone laugh, to a point where the inebriate was making a fool of himself. Clearly, this was a complex interaction in which each participant egged on the other.

While anger and its relatives make up the dominant emotional tone toward alcoholics, they are certainly not the only reactions. Many people accept the alcoholic, sympathize with him, and treat him as they would any other individual with a chronic and partially incapacitating illness—they are not particularly put off by the alcoholic's irresponsibility, his dependence, or his loss of self-control. Although they may not approve of his behavior, they do not chastise him, they do not adopt a tone of moral superiority, nor do they reject him for being alcoholic.

A woman I know employs a man with a severe alcoholic problem to do heavy housecleaning chores. When drinking, he often gets into barrom brawls, and every once in a while he disappears for a month or two, presumably to serve a sentence. An excellent worker, he nearly always arrives sober. My friend has never censured him for his general behavior, has tried to help by trying to get him into treatment, and has done various favors for him. Nevertheless, she makes it quite clear to him that she will not allow him to drink when working. On the occasions when he has drunk on the job she has let him go, but the interesting thing is that he always comes back to her for a job, despite the fact that his services are in great demand. She sympathizes with his plight, but does not see him as a moral leper.

The detached sympathy of such persons, along with their capacity to draw personal boundaries they will not allow others to overstep, is a rare quality, highly beneficial to alcoholics. As we already know, they react against it by repeatedly testing the solidity of barriers, but in the long run they benefit greatly from them. Detached love and a firm setting of limits are largely absent in our relations to alcoholics and other disturbed persons, but are the rule in our relations to children, especially in parent-child relations. It is not for lack of a basic capacity that we fail to adopt this tone with alcoholics, otherwise we could not assume it with children. Its absence with alcoholics underscores our difficulty in accepting childish behavior in adults: "He should know better."

Many clergymen, nurses, and social workers assume sympathetic but firm attitudes towards alcoholics, as do most of those whose primary professional responsibility is to help alcoholics and their families. Some arrive at this naturally, without a second thought, and they are fortunate. Others have to struggle with themselves, principally with their regressive wishes for the fantasied freedom of childhood, before they can arrive at positions where their needs do not affect their feelings toward the alcoholic in ways ultimately adverse for him.

There are those of us, however, who try to solve personal issues through encounters with alcoholics. I am thinking here of the person who attempts to relieve his guilt about feeling angry at an alcoholic by being nice to him, a common pattern among people who devote themselves to uplifting the afflicted. The alcoholic for his part is hardly taken in by good deeds of which the primary purpose is guilt relief; those who act this way will not gain his confidence, although he may unconsciously use them defensively. If he is cynical about do-gooders, guilt-relievers will confirm him.

That needs to help are interwoven with anger is evident in the behavior of a sympathetic and sophisticated doctor I heard about the other day. He had pulled an alcoholic patient through several medical crises only to have his successes ruined by the patient's inability to stop drinking. Following a recent episode, the patient required nursing care at home; no sooner was he home than he began drinking, and another crisis ensued. The doctor vented his fury on the nurse for allowing the patient to drink, but when the nurse pointed out that she had not been told about any alcohol problem, the doctor with shocked innocence replied, "Oh, I couldn't do that. If you knew he was an alcoholic, you might have gotten angry at him."

10

TREATMENT AND ITS EFFECT

TREATMENT OF alcoholism by purely medical means, like drugs, electroshock, and other essentially physical or chemical techniques is not popular now, except in treating the physical consequences of alcoholism. No treatment now in frequent use attacks the alcoholic process at a biochemical or physiological level per se, although from time to time such therapies have been proposed. The primary current physicalistic theory postulates that alcoholism is the result of a vitamin deficiency—which vitamin is not stated. The theory's innovator and chief proponent claims that the alcoholic's craving for alcohol is diminished to a problem-free point when he is given glutaminic acid. This therapy finds little favor in most medical circles, and one observer has said that the theory is incapable of proof or disproof.

Enjoying some popularity now are three chemotherapies, each based on chemically manipulated psychological factors. The first, treatment with antabuse, is based on the patient's knowledge that if he takes a drink he will become horribly ill. Also known as disulfiram, antabuse is taken by mouth and is perfectly harmless if no alcohol is ingested for four days afterward; during those four days a sip of alcohol results in a toxic state resembling shock. Since the physical reaction is severe, only well-motivated, non-impulsive alcoholics should take antabuse; problem drinkers who meet these criteria can usually stop drinking without medicine.

Aversion therapy, another chemical treatment, finds its theoretical origins in the theory of conditioning. Treatment follows the idea that if alcohol is regularly accompanied by extreme physical discomfort or intense fear, eventually its taste, smell, and even sight will arouse the noxious reaction. Rather than experience the discomfort or fear, the alcoholic will renounce alcohol. The more commonly employed substances are apomorphine or emetine, which produce vomiting. After taking the medicine and just prior to vomiting, the person is given a drink. A more recent innovation is succinylcholine, which paralyzes the muscles so that the subject cannot breathe for half a minute or more. The inability to breathe is accompanied, as one may imagine, by fear approaching panic. Alcohol tasted just prior to paralysis presumably becomes associated with the fear attendant upon it.

Another drug treatment, lysergic acid diethylamide, or LSD, has not been widely used. Its proponents suggest that LSD breaks through psychological barriers and rigidities, allows the patient to see aspects of himself from vantage points that permit integration at a different level of functioning. He also may become more amenable than before to participation in other aspects of treatment. So far, however, no clear-cut rationale has been given for the use of LSD as a therapeutic agent.

Other drugs used in the treatment of alcoholics are usually part of a comprehensive-treatment plan. Librium, for example, may be used to control anxiety, or an antidepressant to relieve depression, along with psychotherapy or other therapeutic measures. Although numerous medical steps may be taken to alleviate organic disturbances indirectly linked to excessive use of alcohol, no distinctively medical treatment exists to subvert the alcoholic process.

Psychological forms of treatment include individual and group psychotherapy primarily, although psychodrama, hypnosis, and behavior therapy have been proposed and used with alcoholic patients. Since individual and group psychotherapy are so often loosely defined, one is hard put to know the nature of the treatment unless it is specified in some detail. Individual psychotherapy can include full-scale psychoanalysis, intensive psychotherapy, brief psychotherapy, casework, counseling, or supportive psychotherapy, to mention the more common psychotherapies. How to tell one from another? And which are best suited to alcoholics?

Psychoanalysis, in its classic five-hours-a-week-on-the-couch form, is not the best treatment for alcoholics. Frustration necessarily accompanies psychoanalysis, with few concrete manifestations of personal warmth on the analyst's part. This runs counter to the alcoholic's need for relatively immediate gratification and his desire for open and obvious acceptance. Some professionals have stated categorically that psychoanalysis is useless as a treatment for alcoholism; but this is a misleading distortion. The professional literature contains detailed accounts of successful treatment of alcoholics by traditional psychoanalytic methods. Further, the technical and conceptual apparatus that constitutes the basis for other forms of psychotherapy for alcoholics is derived from psychoanalytic practice and theory. Vehement denials of the utility of psychoanalysis in conceptualizing and treating alcoholism, unaccompanied by rational refutations of analytic positions, may point to difficulty in accepting that the alcoholic's consumption of alcohol is beyond his psychological control.

The distinction between intensive psychotherapy and psychoanalysis is one of degree rather than of substance. As its name implies, meetings between patient and therapist in intensive psychotherapy are frequent, ranging from two to four times a week, and they are usually face to face. Therapy, like analysis, is lengthy, usually not less than two and as much as five or even more years. Aims of treatment are usually as broad as those for analysis, having to do with alterations in personality structure so that the patient can live up to his potentials, form relationships that are satisfying

136

and respectful, and accept his limits. As a goal, relief from symptoms takes a back seat since it is assumed that if primary goals are reached, symptoms will have long since disappeared. As with analysis itself and for the same reasons, intensive psychotherapy is used sparingly with alcoholics.

Frequency of contact is not critical in distinguishing psychoanalysis and intensive psychotherapy from other psychotherapeutic methods. In supportive therapy, patients are sometimes seen daily at first to foster a strong alliance between patient and therapist or to help the alcoholic over a crisis. Of course, frequent meetings over a period of years accurately describe intensive, character-reforming kinds of therapy and distinguish them from those with other, perhaps less ambitious, aims.

Brief psychotherapy, which has many varieties, aims at understanding in depth a particular, well-defined problem or symptom. Its cardinal rule says that problems or issues not directly related to the one at hand are ignored; or at least the therapist does not make any active attempt to explore them, but keeps the patient focused on the primary issue. Those who respond well to brief psychotherapeutic methods are typically well-endowed socially and psychologically. Their problems have come on rather suddenly following a readily discernible stress, and they have not been disturbed for any length of time. By most standards they are healthy. Brief psychotherapeutic sessions usually take place weekly for periods lasting from three months to a year. The therapist in most forms of brief psychotherapy acts like the analyst, except that he usually searches and probes for feelings and thoughts relevant to the patient's problem. Brief psychotherapy is not frequently recommended for alcoholics; it runs counter to their avoidance of sudden challenges to their inner fortress.

Casework is what social workers call that psychotherapeutic process which focuses on interpersonal relations and "reality" problems. Casework utilizes psychoanalytic understanding of the patient and his life history to help him cope in self-satisfying ways with his problems. Current conflicts and the patient's solutions of them are understood by the caseworker to be variations of earlier-life conflicts and previously learned solutions, but the social worker ordinarily does not seek out memories and fantasies of childhood as the analyst does. The goal is to help the patient respond to present conflict flexibly, so that he can select the most relevant and appropriate solution.

Two critical points of casework practice merit special notice in light of our interest in treating alcoholics. First, the caseworker tries to form a positive, trusting relationship with his client, and in this he will be much more active and "natural" than the analyst or psychotherapist. Client and caseworker may chat informally over coffee about areas in a patient's life that seem to have little or nothing to do with his problem. The social worker is openly sympathetic and expresses concern about a patient's daily trials and tribulations and freely goes to lengths analysts consider extreme in order to ensure a warm, positive relationship. Second, the caseworker does not hesitate to offer or arrange for concrete services where it is clear that the need for them is common sense or a necessary part of treatment. A patient was unable to come to his social worker by public transportation because his leg was in a cast and he could not afford taxi fare; the social worker arranged to have the cab fare paid.

Casework is a form of treatment that offers much to alcoholics. Counseling and supportive psychotherapy are like casework in their applicability to problems of alcoholics. Casework, however, refers to a more generally accepted and delimited framework of practice than either counseling or supportive therapy; both terms are loosely used and may be employed to refer to widely differing treatment techniques. What I mean by counseling or supportive therapy varies from what Dr. Jones down the street means, and indeed Dr. Smith across town agrees with neither of us.

For me, supportive therapy, like casework, includes the rendering of concrete services and the establishment of a warm trusting relationship. But the therapeutic focus is less on aiding a patient to come to grips with each situation in its own terms than on strengthening personality assets and shoring up areas of previous strength now in danger of collapse. I recently saw a man of ability who was about to take a new job that he felt would be personally rewarding to him. He wanted the job, but he was afraid that he would find the responsibilities involved constraining and too great a burden; his anxiety was so strong that he thought of refusing the job offer. He felt he was childish to think this way, but he could not forget two other occasions where he gave up under similar strains. As he talked things over with me, I saw that he failed whenever he felt he was completely on his own; because his father was a weak man, he—the patient—had to fend for himself when he was growing up. He also told me that as soon as he made the appointment to see me, he felt better. At the close of our first meeting, I commented that I would be pleased to work together with him on his problem, that I was behind him, and that we could work it out together. My emphasis on working together and backing him up was a straightforward supportive measure. He took the job and, after an initial period of anxiety, got down to work; as he had prophesied, he got increasing satisfaction from his work, and stopped seeing me: the support of a man like he wished his father was was no longer necessary to him.

Any discussion of group psychotherapy must be prefaced by distinguishing between group experiences with and those without specific therapeutic goals. For example, T-groups (T for training) are groups of individuals who share an interest in understanding group dynamics for practical application, such as understanding the processes whereby a committee comes to a decision or how a group of workers interacts. T-groups are also used to train leaders for other groups. The purpose of T-groups is usually self-expression; members are supposed to say what they feel, what they think of other group members, and so on. The leader assumes a minimal role, encouraging spontaneity of expression by group members. Though these groups have no avowed therapeutic aim, their participants often think of them as psychotherapy groups. Another example is the Alcoholics Anonymous group meeting, frequently referred to as group psychotherapy. These group meetings do indeed serve a therapeutic function, but they are not a form of group psychotherapy except in a generic sense that has little in common with generally accepted technical definitions of group psychotherapy.

thank god

There are a number of schools of thought about group therapy: the distinctions are often doctrinaire. Broadly speaking, group psychotherapy has two main functions. First, the group experience demonstrates to the individual that he is not alone in his thoughts and fantasies about himself and teaches him something about how people get along in groups and social situations. In these terms, it is particularly appropriate for shy, lonely, introverted people, as well as for extroverts who have little inner sense about their impact on others. As useful and important as this function is, the second reason for therapeutic groups is that they undoubtedly serve to effect basic personality changes. This function requires a group member to play out in a contemporary and protected setting unresolved conflicts of early life, with other group members playing the parts of persons—mother and father, sister and brother—who were in his mind important to him as a child. In this repeated playing-out, with roles constantly shifting, the patient resolves early conflicts. He gradually comes to see the group interaction as a process that one participates in on the basis of what is happening now rather than what happened then.

Group psychotherapy is particularly fashionable in treating alcoholics. Whether its popularity is warranted is another question. Certainly, its first function less than its second makes it appro-

140

TREATMENT AND ITS EFFECT

priate for alcoholics. Or perhaps its major value is making a limited number of therapists available to a greater number of patients.

Another form of group treatment, known as psychodrama, capitalizes on the playing-out function of group therapy, using it directly as a quasi-dramatic technique. The group leader or "director" assigns roles to members of the group, or "audience," to re-enact an event recalled by one of the members of the group. For example, a patient relates a childhood memory of trying to protect his mother from the attacks of his drunken father. The patient may be asked to play himself as a small boy, as two other patients act the parts of the mother and father. Through re-enactment, submerged feelings may be expressed and new more satisfying ways of dealing with the problem learned. Highly dramatic, and stimulating powerful feelings, a psychodrama session can get out of hand; also, its sensationalistic nature tends to attract practitioners insufficiently trained in its use.

Hypnosis in treating problem drinking has followed two paths. The more common involves a direct attack on the compulsion to drink through posthypnotic suggestions that the subject will have no desire for alcohol when he awakens from the trance. The other employs a hypnotic or highly relaxed state of being as an aid in recovering memories and feelings suppressed in more alert states of consciousness. Despite reports of dramatic cures for many kinds of psychological symptoms, hypnosis is generally considered ineffective to eliminate symptoms by suggestion. As a technical aid in individual psychotherapy, however, hypnosis has much to recommend it; with patients receptive to the hypnotic experience it is very useful in some mental disorders. Its effectiveness with alcoholics is open to question because the alcoholic is usually not amenable to hypnotic suggestion, being far too vigilant to permit himself to be "controlled" by another. It would be interesting to determine if openly dependent alcoholics were more receptive to hypnotic induction than counterdependent alcoholics; a priori, this would seem to be the case.

The behavior therapies, based on principles of learning theory, are also used in treating alcoholics. Learning theory represents one of psychology's attempts to explain how and why man learns. Because of the relative ease with which crucial factors can be manipulated in the laboratory, most of the basic work of the various theorists has been in animal experimentation. Models of learning employed in, and growing out of, experiments with animals were usually developed with one scientific eye on their relevance for explaining human learning. Many of these models have been applied to humans to explain neurotic symptoms, among other things. Aversion therapy, with apomorphine, or with succinylcholine, is based on one principle of learning theory, conditioning, first discovered by the Russian psychophysiologist Pavlov around the turn of the century. Most of the behavior therapies used with alcoholics create an association between alcohol and a highly repellent stimulus, such as vomiting, fear of an inability to breathe, or a painful electric shock. The association is strengthened by repetition to a point, so the theory goes, where the rewards of drinking alcohol are less than the rewards of not drinking it, that is, of escaping pain or panic. Persons willing to undergo such medieval experiences in order to give up alcohol could probably reach the same goal by submitting to less inhumane methods. In speaking of treatment of alcoholics, the question of motivation is always in the fore, and the patient highly motivated to overcome his problem has a high chance of success. Barring a deeper motivation to seek out punishment, patients willing to undergo aversion therapy would seem to be highly motivated.

Behavior therapy appears to have a distinct place in the treatment of certain emotional disorders—phobias in particular. But behavior therapy with phobic persons is substantially different from behavior therapy with problem drinkers. The former applies a carefully thought-out plan which gradually brings the afflicted individual into contact with the feared object. The individual overcomes his fear step by step, and when he falters, the step is repeated until he has confident mastery of it. This differs markedly from aversion therapy.

One last form of "treatment," neither medical nor psychological, I have called social therapy for want of a better term. I refer to Alcoholics Anonymous, for many years now the most common treatment for alcoholism. Widespread reliance on it is in itself a curious phenomenon, especially since we have no sound evidence that A.A. is more effective than other treatments for alcoholism. Huge numbers of alcoholics have been helped through A.A., if for no other reasons than that it is so widely known and attracts large numbers of alcoholics. Perhaps many caretakers send alcoholic clients to A.A. because alcoholics taking care of alcoholics means fewer to disturb the professional. The commonly given verbal reason for referral to A.A. is the statement: "Where else could I send him? A.A. is the only resource we have." In many instances A.A. is not the only resource. This is leper-colony thinking.

Why does A.A. work for some, but not for others? First, A.A. groups are an exclusive subsociety of people devoted to the nonuse of alcohol. In the larger society, drinking is sanctioned and even encouraged, but in A.A. it is discouraged and not sanctioned. The deviant, drinking A.A. member, however, is not punished or rejected. Second, the individual finds it difficult to retreat within himself, for in addition to his "sponsor," he is called and visited by other members; this attention accelerates when a slip appears to be in the offing. Third, a new member can often relax when he discovers that his self-deceptions and the masks he puts on for family, boss, and so on are thoroughly familiar to fellow members. Finally, support of the group and the experience of expiation through confession in front of a group can have a salutary effect, although a shy person may be frightened off by demands to speak before a group. Insistence on spiritual elements in the A.A. movement is a potentially negative aspect for some members; A.A. members will tell you that the movement is open-minded about religion, but group pressures are strong, and an alcoholic is rarely considered a full-fledged member until he accepts A.A.'s spiritual outlook.

A.A. has been criticized by some psychologists and psychiatrists who claim that it is "repressive" insofar as it aims toward burying conflicts deeper rather than bringing them to light where they may be understood and solved. And this is undoubtedly true of many A.A. groups and members. Often enough, one sees an A.A. "success" who has simply shifted his addiction from alcohol to A.A. From social and economic viewpoints this is all to the good, but the alcoholic's mental health may be as impaired as before. Signs, though, point to a shift away from a "repressive" orientation. One notes, for example, more emphasis than before on inner examination of oneself. In the A.A. magazine, *The Grapevine,* articles frequently appear on psychological and personality factors in alcoholism. The increased emphasis on inner experience will probably ultimately strengthen the effectiveness of A.A. New and younger members, reared in our psychological age, are providing a major impetus for this shift.

Specific treatment techniques must necessarily be summarized one by one, giving a misleading impression of separateness of application. In reality, the therapies are seldom used in isolation. Ideally, a comprehensive plan is made for each patient, taking into account his strengths, weaknesses, life situation, family, and work. In practice many treatment facilities offer patients combinations of the therapies described above, although each doctor and each agency ordinarily has its own favorite therapeutic specialty. There are, unfortunately, some institutions where, because of lack of staff or interest, alcoholics get no treatment other than being kept away from alcohol.

Having heard various therapies described, what can we now say of their effectiveness? Are increasing numbers of alcoholics being salvaged and rehabilitated as the number of facilities designed for their aid rises? Is the proportion of alcoholics in America decreasing as treatment efforts intensify? Sad to report, there is no evidence to suggest that the percentage of alcoholics in the population has decreased, despite the fact that the absolute numbers of alcoholics being successfully treated now is greater than ever before. Treatment endeavors have made not the slightest dent in the alcohol problem as a social entity, although many individual successes occur.

The explanation of this anomalous situation may be found in two related factors. First, few alcoholics ever get to a treatment facility. Why? Because, as a society, we fail to identify those sick members of it who are alcoholic; because the afflicted individual fears stigma and shame if he openly admits his problem; and because many areas of the country have no resources other than state hospitals and jails to treat alcoholics. The fact that failure to seek help is not simply a result of lack of therapeutic facilities is proved by the situation in my state, which has an unusually well-supported and active public alcoholism program. Its seventeen clinics, scattered throughout the state, see in a year 9,000 patients, who account for not quite 5 percent of the state's estimated 200,000 persons with alcoholic problems.

Second, only a small fraction of alcoholics who contact a clinic or hospital follow recommendations for treatment. This failure to stick with treatment was named the "dropout" problem long before the term became common in connection with another pressing social problem. While the dropout rate varies from place to place, it generally ranges from 50 to 75 percent of alcoholics referred to a facility. In other words, only 25 to 50 of every 100 patients follow doctor's orders. One bit of information is vitally important here. General estimates state that at least two-thirds of those who stick with treatment are ultimately helped in significant ways. If methods of involving alcoholics in treatment were developed, a substantial proportion of them might become successful participants in treatment. Many observers have interpreted the fact of early termination of treatment as a basic flaw in the alcoholic's desire to help himself. A common cry is that alcoholics are not motivated. This is not necessarily the case, as shown by a study that conclusively demonstrated the success of a method to facilitate and enhance the alcoholic's sometimes tenuous motivation to help himself. Techniques like the ones used in this study are now commonplace at my hospital but have not been generally adopted by other treatment centers.

Assume that the alcoholic follows the caretaker's suggestions for treatment. What, then, is the relative effectiveness for one therapy over another? Research evidence is a poor guide, for it has usually been gathered without much forethought and without the personal detachment requisite to adequate scientific endeavor. After sifting the findings, one is left with the impression that one treatment works as well as another. The more scientifically rigorous investigations usually report the lowest percentage of successful outcomes, sometimes as low as 20 or 30 percent, while some of the less satisfactory inquiries report percentages of success higher than 80 percent. These unpromising figures differ surprisingly little from those reported for chronic physical illnesses. If we think of alcoholism as a chronic condition, then those who care for alcoholics are no more, but no less, effective than those who care for diabetics or the victims of heart disease. Certainly, if we were able to match each patient with the therapy most suitable for him, success rates would be much higher.

Whatever the figures show, the successful practitioner must possess faith in himself and his ability to help others. His belief in his efficacy includes confidence in himself and what he does, a sense of mastery over the technical details of his work, a genuine and unconflicted desire to help those in distress, a concern for the welfare of others, and a willingness and freedom to lay down his professional shield to make contact with another human being out of disinterested love. Patients respond to caretakers who know what they are doing, who are interested, and who can be trusted.

In this chapter, I have described physical, psychological, and social therapies in current use for alcoholics. Treatment programs have had little impact on the extent of alcoholism as a social problem because of the low proportion of alcoholics who ever get into treatment. Once they go into treatment, success is relatively high, but one treatment seems to be no more effective than any other. Decreasing the extent of alcoholism as a social illness will probably prove to be an instance of closing the door before the horse gets out, a possibility I discuss in the next chapter.

11

PREVENTING ALCOHOLISM

ALL GREAT ATTEMPTS to eradicate alcoholism have been preventive. The simplest, most direct way to eradicate trouble is to stop its occurrence. No one questions the truism, but selection of ways and means of attaining its goal has always been controversial.

Gardeners and farmers find weeds a hindrance to the cultivation and production of good flowers and vegetables (even though a well-known comic strip child grows a weed garden, as did a character in a recent spy movie). For a garden to flourish, weeds must be prevented. Over the ages agriculturists and horticulturists have adopted various strategies in attempts to wipe out weeds. Some do it psychologically either by denying that weeds constitute a problem or by hoping in Pollyanna-ish fashion that they will be gone in the morning. Such persons, I might add, are more often amateurs. Some adopt a ritual or ceremonial approach that may or may not find its roots in religion—ceremonies of preliterate peoples to ensure good crops are frankly magical from our viewpoint even though many of us engage in prayer to eradicate weeds. These preventive steps may be classed as irrational global approaches that have had little success in wiping out weeds.

Techniques such as hand weeding and cultivation by hoe or machine have a clearly defined focus of attack. The weeder or cultivator attempts to reduce the prevalence of weeds by killing them at some point during their growth—sometimes early, some-

148

times after the weeds are full grown. The timing of weeding is important on several counts, including crowding of plants and depletion of soil nutrients, but most significant from a preventive standpoint is whether it is done before or after the weed has gone to seed. If after, the aim of prevention is not well served. The way in which weeding is done is critical: weeders who take hoe to row in a state of furious energy may eradicate as many carrots as they do weeds. Preventive measures applied after the weed seed has germinated, or after the weed has started to grow, may be likened to treatment of alcoholism. Treatment of an illness when its symptoms are in full bloom is known as tertiary, or third-level, prevention. Identifying and treating an illness before its symptoms are apparent, but when there is other presumptive evidence of a specifiable disease process, is known as secondary prevention. It is analogous to weeding when a weed first makes its appearance above ground, but long before it has attained full growth or reached the first stage of its reproductive cycle.

Finally, there are methods of managing weeds, not aimed primarily at reducing prevalence of weeds, but at preventing weeds from growing in the first place. These methods are usually based on an analysis of a weed's history from life to death and how the weed relates to its environment. Factors blocking or freeing its growth and reproduction are scrutinized. Employment of the one or reversal of the other may create a break in a weed's life history that results in its decline and eventual demise. For instance, a particular weed cannot grow without a certain nutrient; the preventive weed specialist may keep the nutrient out of a desirable plant's environment, provided that the plant can thrive without it. Preventive endeavors attempting to manipulate conditions so that the problem no longer arises are known collectively as primary prevention.

All methods used by the farmer in his struggles against weeds have been at one time or another used against alcoholism. Neither weeds nor alcoholism seem to have been much affected, though if we were to award prizes for a modicum of success, the agriculturist gets the nod over the alcohologist.

Irrational approaches to preventing alcoholism are undoubtedly common. Despite repeated publicity in newspapers and on radio and television, despite initiation of state programs and inauguration of a national center on alcoholism, an all too frequent query is "What problem?" This question is a close relative to the statements: "Let's not look at it too closely and perhaps it will go away," and "Drunks sure are funny; let's not take them too seriously." Other than these passive and denying views are several active, irrational preventive approaches. The time-honored tertiary preventive mode is punishment and exile, replaced from time to time in Western society by a therapeutic orientation.

The rationale for punishment and exile by imprisonment or other institutionalization is threefold: the miscreant will see the error of his ways; in the meantime his segregation from society will protect its members from being infected or contaminated; finally, he is a public example and warning to others tempted to follow his path. That the punitive approach has had no palpable effect on either the incidence or prevalence of alcoholism, or for that matter on any other mental or social derangement, is ignored and denied by its advocates. This suggests the presence of more compelling reasons for its continuance than its classical rationale, reasons having to do with fear, anger, and cruelty. The occasional upsurge of countervailing therapeutic modes, as are in ascendancy now (and were also in vogue around the turn of the century, as represented by the Washingtonian movement), is explained by the play of social forces.

Other than the treatments of alcoholism described in the last chapter, no scientifically responsible and population-wide attempts at prevention have been made. Prohibition was a gallant but misguided and simplistic attempt to prevent alcoholism by eradicating the use of alcohol. The disaster following enactment of the Eighteenth Amendment was hardly counterbalanced by the fact that it weakened, permanently I trust, militant temperance groups. The aim of prohibition of course was not to solve the alcoholism problem, but to end the sinful practice of drinking. It seems amazing now that prohibition could ever have come about, and it could not have happened except for a coalition of strange bedfellows. The militant, but relatively small, group that favored total abstinence could never alone have made prohibition a social reality. But this group rallied behind it strong support from religious bodies ambivalent about the use of alcohol, from groups that were not against the use of liquor but its immoderate use or against other groups who frankly favored the use of alcohol, and from well-intentioned but naïve souls who believed that prohibiting alcohol would bring about a cessation of alcoholism.

The reversal of the ill-fated attempt at prevention has had little effect on some states and communities, which either continue to be islands of prohibition or restrict the quantity of alcohol sold. The only other broad attempts at prevention since prohibition may be found in the law books of most states. Enacted statutes require that children participate in "alcohol education" programs as part of public school attendance. Implementation of these laws has been less than satisfactory; often courses are not given, and when they are, they are led by untrained instructors who focus on the "evils" of alcohol or who approach the course with a derisive attitude about "drunks."

Perhaps we can learn from our failures. Certainly our chances of preventing alcoholism seem more optimistic because of a series of interconnected events, notably, the Community Mental Health Centers Acts of 1963, the war on poverty, and the establishment in 1966 of a national center to control and prevent alcoholism. These events are legislative reflections of broad humanistic conceptions about the best strategies for attacking social problems. One idea is that programs which radically transform a young child's environment can change the entire direction of his life, an idea guiding the Head Start program and other educational innovations. Conceptions like this originated from research findings and theoretical observations of social scientists and social philosophers, based on their analyses of forces at play in social problems. Thinking of this kind is now more apparent in the work and ideas of those professionally concerned with alcoholism and alcoholics. While recognizing needs to treat full-blown alcoholics, these professionals want to redeploy resources for primary and secondary preventive purposes.

What are some of the exciting and promising preventive trends now taking shape? The public school setting seems a logical place to make population-wide efforts to change attitudes and reduce ambivalence about using alcohol. I have alluded to the failure of our schools to educate children about alcohol. Not long ago, however, Allen Williams directed a small experimental program with youngsters, taking careful pains to evaluate its outcome. The "course," one week long, was designed to avoid the boredom of a lecture by an apathetic and uninformed teacher. It was led by persons knowledgeable about the psychological and physical effects of alcohol used socially and immoderately; the teachers were experienced in leading small group discussions that place a premium on an exchange of ideas, information, and feelings. Eight to ten junior high school pupils met for five days in succession to talk about drinking. The interest level of students was high, and lively exchanges occurred in each group.

The children's attitudes toward drinking, their factual knowledge about alcohol and its effects, and reports of their own drinking behavior were obtained before and after the educational experience. To see how long the effect of learning lasted, measures were repeated several times for a year. To guard against the possibility that whatever learning occurred might result from experiences other

152

than group discussion, Williams also examined children who talked about current affairs instead of about drinking.

The discussion groups were effective over the short term in lessening negative attitudes about alcohol use: for a while the children no longer felt that drinking was a terribly sinful and evil practice. After the educational experience, the children knew distinctly more facts about alcohol than they had before, and they retained this knowledge longer than their changed feelings about its use. Most interesting, however, were the findings about drinking behavior. In the year following group discussion the youngsters who talked about drinking reported that they had experimented in using alcohol themselves far more often than the children who talked about current affairs. It was as if talking about alcohol and its effects led these children to try it out themselves more frequently. If this were the only finding on the children's behavior, we might find the approach useless, but when we look at the youngster's reports about getting "high" or "drunk," a different picture emerges. More current-affairs than drinking-discussion children said they got drunk repeatedly during the year. Unguided exposure to alcohol results in poor judgment in its use, whereas guided introduction to it results in healthy patterns of use. This unique study shows that a relatively simple and inexpensive educational technique, taking little away from wider educational aims, can have a beneficial and fairly lasting effect on drinking behavior and knowledge about it.

Another avenue to prevention not dissimilar to the one above (except that it is a suggestive discursion instead of an evaluation of a specific application) has been proposed by Morris Chafetz on the basis of his analysis of drinking in societies that consume a great deal of alcohol with little attendant problem. He observed that heavy-drinking but nonalcoholic peoples drink slowly, sipping their drinks in a relaxed manner in a relaxing setting with other people; they drink only while eating, and invariably while seated, and do not become inebriated. Among such peoples—the Italians for one, the Lebanese for another—intoxication is frowned upon and is not a source of amusement, but of unambiguous disapproval. He contrasts these practices and attitudes with those of Americans: fast drinking, fast talking, and fast acting; drinking seldom accompanying eating; inner tenseness and a supercharged atmosphere; and intoxication more often condoned than condemned.

Based on his analysis, Chafetz has suggested that young people be given courses which show the effect of these elements on drinking and their relation to mental and bodily well-being. As part of the course material, he has proposed the possibility of a "practicum" in which drinking experience occurs within an attitudinally neutral educational setting. He encourages extension of a practice common to some colleges, that of a late-afternoon sherry and of providing beer and wine with meals.

Proposals like this and educational techniques like the group-discussion method are based on a reasoned examination of social and psychological factors involved in excessive and social use of alcohol. Young people have strong feelings about things forbidden to them but not to grownups, especially when adults show that the activity is pleasurable, and yet somehow wrong. Laws restricting young men and women from purchasing alcohol lead to much surreptitious, semilegal, if not illegal, maneuvering that in and of itself is reprehensible. Since the teen-ager is not supposed to have alcohol, when he does drink he is apt to be like a child at a cookie jar: fearful, greedy, and hasty. In this sense, restrictive legislation and mores indirectly cause unhealthy drinking among young people. Repeated surreptitious thrill drinking may further create an association between quick and greedy drinking on the one hand and, on the other, an attitude that says, "Look at what I'm getting away with!"

Answers to questions of what young people think about alcohol and its effects define an important but largely neglected area of potential prevention. A person's preconceptions about alcohol may determine his response to it as much as, or even more than, his response to alcohol itself. Who has not heard a person at a cocktail party turn down a Martini for a Manhattan with the statement, "Oh, I love Martinis, but I just can't drink them—they really knock me for a loop." As a matter of taste, fine, but pharmacologically there is barely a difference between the two. The Martini phenomenon is a result of what we lead ourselves to expect; we do not respond simply to the substance "Martini," but to the label "Martini" as well, with all that it conjures up in our minds.

Young people—and older ones, too—have all sorts of ideas about alcohol. Rather Lindner dubbed them the "romance" of alcohol. They include the beliefs that alcohol enhances sexual prowess and attractiveness, makes the weak strong, and the cowardly brave; that it is a prelude to excitement, adventure, and fun; and that it makes the awkward skillful and the unhappy happy. All of these touch on issues that anguish adolescents, who are trying out capacities, with roller-coaster ups and downs in feelings. In the down swing, when the stomach sinks, the adolescent turns in every direction to prove his worth to others and to himself. He is vulnerable to imbibing a potion that promises to give him all that he feels he lacks.

If paths along which these myths are communicated could be mapped, we might be able to set up roadblocks to impede their transmission. In part, the group sessions described above serve this purpose by presenting a rational and factual view of alcohol, but whether this serves as a substitute for fantasy is uncertain. Reason and fantasy about alcohol coexist. Transmission of these myths occurs partly through television and movies, and partly by one adolescent initiating another. Transmission of cultural values and norms is usually thought of as taking place between one generation and the next: from parent to child, from teacher to pupil. But alcohol myths about enhancing personal worth and prowess seldom take this avenue. Other myths about alcohol—such as "It is bad for you" or "It will ruin your health"—probably are handed down from one generation to the next. They are also less influential in determining experimental behavior with alcohol than fun-oriented myths transmitted from adolescent to adolescent. Once cultural myths and means of their dissemination are identified, the way is open to short-circuiting paths permitting passage of irrational, ambivalent expectations about alcohol that appear linked to growth of alcohol pathology.

Methods of primary prevention of alcoholism are incompletely effective unless accompanied by techniques of secondary prevention: those methods of removing alcoholic weeds when they are about to make their appearance, but before they reach full growth. The first task of secondary prevention is to identify groups of people who run a high risk of becoming alcoholic. When persons susceptible to the alcoholism "bug" have been identified, the next task of secondary prevention is to increase their resistance to alcoholism. Where do we stand on the first task? Who runs a high risk of becoming alcoholic?

In the past few years, investigators in widely dispersed sections of the United States and Canada have been gathering information about drinking practices of young people in high school and college. We now know with some certainty the proportion of young people who drink, the age at which they start to drink, the percentage who get "high," and so on. In public health parlance, the descriptive epidemiology of teen-age drinking practices is virtually complete. More teen-agers than ever before are drinking and drinking at younger ages, but the proportion of youngsters who drink in excessive ways remains constant and relatively small. This percentage, nevertheless, is important because it includes those young persons for whom chances of having an adult problem with alcohol are high. These youngsters, who may be tomorrow's alcoholics, are high-risk or susceptible persons.

PREVENTING ALCOHOLISM

George Maddox, studying collegiate drinking behavior in a southern community, inadvertently found that students who suffered accidental injuries were nearly always drinking at the time. Pursuing the association, he found the injured person is typically a heavy drinker, preoccupied with alcohol, who drinks primarily for the kicks he gets from it. When he tested students who hurt themselves, he found that they had more problems with alcohol than students who had not injured themselves. As Maddox suggests, among youths, accidents while drinking may be an "alerting sign" to the presence of a potentially severe, but symptomatically nascent, drinking problem.

A commonly accepted though not incontestably proven tenet among alcohologists is that children of alcoholics have a high chance of becoming alcoholics when they grow up. About one-half of the alcoholics seen in clinics and hospitals report that one of their parents or another relative important to them in their formative years was alcoholic. Family tension, strife, and bitterness; repeated scenes of remorse, forgiveness, and new resolve; and threats of corporal abuse and punishment are the lot of children in a family with an alcoholic member. Chances for these youngsters to become emotionally or socially deviant are high. Most workers in the field have failed to concern themselves with the broader implication of growing up in a disorganized family setting, but have been content to focus more narrowly on transmission of alcoholism from parent to child. No one today entertains a belief that this transmission is biologically hereditary; it is generally agreed that transmission occurs through learning. The little boy *learns* to be like his father; he is not born like him. Despite knowledge that alcoholism may be handed down from one generation to the next, virtually nothing has been done to try to interrupt the process. Alateen groups, composed of teen-age children of alcoholics, serve a preventive function, but the groups were initiated without thought of preventive implications.

157

A third group of youngsters who may be headed for alcoholic careers are delinquents who misbehave while drinking, or who are adjudged delinquent for the offense of public drunkenness. In a study upon which my colleagues and I are at present engaged, we will find out whether drinking delinquents become alcoholic as adults, and also whether psychological treatment during adolescence affects the frequency with which subsequent alcoholism occurs. In addition to teen-agers who are injured while drinking, children of alcoholics, and drinking delinquents, one might look at college students in academic or administrative difficulty, Monday morning absentees, and persons in automobile accidents as groups in which to seek potential alcoholics.

Once we have identified persons at risk, what can we offer them? What *should* we offer them? We have an obligation, at the risk of being called busybodies, to let them know that they run a greater risk than the next fellow of developing an alcoholic problem. After that, provisions can be made for thoroughgoing psychological and social evaluation, if desired. Such an evaluation would in many instances show no problem to be present. Thereafter periodic re-evaluations could be offered to guard against the possibility of a problem getting started and well-entrenched; if problems appeared on checkup, treatment fitting the condition could be recommended. This approach is preventive maintenance. Should evaluation reveal clear-cut presence of a problem or other difficulties, plans could be set in motion for appropriate treatment.

Group-counseling approaches which aim both at imparting information and achieving self-understanding are promising in working with teen-agers who are essentially within the normal range of psychological and social behavior. Economical modes of intervention at an early age can save a great deal of money later on, but, more significantly, they will reduce heartache and pain for the individual and suffering for his family.

In this and the previous two chapters, we have moved away

158

from an immediate concern with the personality of the alcoholic to speak of our feelings about him, the kinds of therapy he receives, and the possibilities of preventing alcoholic casualties. Yet our conception of the personality of the alcoholic is linked to attitudes, treatment, and prevention. Attitudes we hold about the alcoholic have complex origins, but they form, and are formed by, the interwoven personal filaments within the alcoholic and within us. Learning about the alcoholic and how we feel about him has, as one aim, his more effective treatment and, as another, the prevention of alcoholism.

12

CONCLUSION

THIS BOOK has dealt with the personality of the alcoholic. I have attempted to construct a framework whereby the problem drinker, his loved ones, and those who are in positions conducive to helping him can understand his behavior. From understanding and knowledge come control. I have used the concept of dependency as my basic building matter. Conflict and anxiety about the gratification of needs to depend on others is a core issue for most alcoholics. It is the way in which he resolves this conflict that is a major key to understanding the actions of the individual alcoholic. I have suggested that the three common methods of resolving dependency conflict result in three distinctive behavioral patterns among alcoholics. The three classes are the dependent, the counterdependent and the dependent-independent alcoholics. Most personality characteristics commonly ascribed to alcoholics may be understood within this threefold scheme.

The depressive features of many alcoholics can be seen as anger turned upon the self. Anger itself is both a consequence and reflection of the extent to which dependent needs have been frustrated, while turning them against the self, rather than expressing them outwardly or harnessing them for one's self-interest, is itself an inner necessity based on fear of loss of dependent satisfactions. If one expresses anger, one may be rejected and lose whatever passive satisfactions one is receiving.

CONCLUSION

Denial is one of the traditional 3-D's of alcoholism: dependency, depression, and denial. Its relation to dependency needs is complex, but one thing is clear: the greater the anxiety about being dependent, the greater the denial. The alcoholic who needs to present himself as masculine, independent, and self-reliant denies his problem with alcohol, for to admit it would mean to subvert the image he creates for himself and those around him.

The alcoholic's proverbial inability to withstand frustration, along with his proclivity to act on impulse, is closely linked to a failure to socialize dependent drives. The failure to learn how to modulate dependency needs is in part the product of the disfavor society holds for expression of avowedly passive and dependent behavior among men. A factor that undoubtedly adds its part to socialization failures lies in lack of fulfillment of dependent needs in childhood. Nonfulfillment, or frustration, of a need theoretically increases its intensity. The unfed child gets hungrier. The impulse becomes stronger. This in part explains why the alcoholic grabs what he can when he can, and why he finds it difficult to brook slight interferences to the pursuit of his goals.

The alcoholic is as noted for his bravura as for his manifestations of self-disgust, and while both may be seen either as an expression of or as a defense against depression, they may profitably be viewed as functions of alternating self-perceptions of one's wishes to depend on others and the alcoholic's failure to make a clear-cut developmental distinction between self and not-self. The alcoholic, more than most of us, tends in crisis to live through again early feelings, attitudes, and dispositions of hated helplessness on the one hand and omnipotence on the other.

Dependency plays an important part in marriage, friendship, and other less enduring relationships with people. The alcoholic's relations with others are only incompletely satisfying to him. If openly dependent, he is apt to make demands that most relationships are unable to survive. If counterdependent, he is sufficiently

161

frightened by closeness and warmth so that his relationships are typified by superficiality and transiency, with occasional short-lived forays into emotional depths from which he must quickly escape. Gregariousness rather than seclusiveness is the natural bent of the alcoholic, but gregariousness says nothing of the depth of a relationship, just as solitary drinking is not necessarily a hallmark of seclusiveness.

Throughout the discussion of personality traits of alcoholics and their linkage to dependency needs and wishes, I have wherever possible indicated how an understanding of the origins of the traits can be put to use in helping alcoholics.

Of particular importance in this regard is a failure to appreciate and take into account the alcoholic's desire to overcome his problem because we are blinded to it by his importunities on us. This is not to say that we should act and feel as if his provocative but self-destructive actions were nonexistent, but that we should not let them obscure our vision to a point where we neglect the fact that a sick man, wishing help but afraid to ask for it, faces us. Emphasis is placed on continuity and consistency of care, respect for individual integrity and dignity, and awakening dormant desires toward health.

Much of the book deals with alcoholic men, because alcoholism is proportionately a problem of men, because the dependency framework is not as satisfactory when applied to the personality of alcoholic women as when applied to men, and because my experience and that of others is richer with regard to male than to female problem-drinkers. When we do consider the instance of the woman with an alcohol problem, we find that the socially formed magical bond between alcohol and man is not nearly so intense among women. The woman, far more than the man, uses alcohol for its physical effects of deadening the onslaught of a hard world or the pain of an inner conflict. In a word, she uses it like a medicine.

CONCLUSION

The unhealthy use of alcohol by women, as well as the unhealthy use of drugs and sex, results from the ambiguous position of women in Western society. She grows up in a nominally sexually liberated world, with family and schools telling her that the world is her oyster. Only when she finishes college or earns a graduate degree, does she discover that there are two worlds, one for men, the other for women. The ensuing disappointment may be coped with in any number of ways. One route leads to alcoholism.

In the latter part of the book I departed from direct examination of the personality of the alcoholic to consider some of the emotional and social causes of the tradition that says that alcoholics are bad, rather than sick, and should be laughed at or despised, rather than understood. Our attitudes and behavior toward alcoholics and alcoholism bear an intimate connection with treatment issues, affecting which alcoholics get into treatment and which do not, and also affecting the selection of therapies available to the alcoholic. I know of no psychosocial disorder, for example, in which one's conscious control of breathing is taken away so as to allow panic and symptom to coexist, in the hope that fear will drive the demon symptom away. Because of narrow stereotypes held about the nature and characteristics of alcoholism, many alcoholics are ashamed to seek treatment; others who seek it are passed by and in effect denied treatment. It is generally agreed that the best form of treatment is a comprehensive plan that takes emotional, social, and physical realities into account on an individual, case-by-case basis. Treatment that fails to consider personality factors is usually foredoomed. Nevertheless, no one kind of therapy is a cure-all as far as alcoholism is concerned. A common denominator of success of treatment of alcoholism, whether it be psychological or not, is the enthusiasm and belief in efficacy with which it is applied. For this reason demagogic types of therapy may prove highly successful, although only when "true believers" practice them.

The hope for solving the alcoholism problem on a wide societal basis lies not with treatment, however, but with preventing its onset in the first place, and identifying and treating alcohol problems when they are incipient rather than full grown. These are technically called primary and secondary prevention respectively. We are now entering a period where I fully expect massive attempts at primary and secondary prevention to take place. There are signs of a quickening of independently arrived at, rational suggestions for changing societal attitudes toward alcohol and its use, of instituting innovative educational programs in primary and secondary grades, and of identifying and treating segments of our youth who appear to run a high risk of developing alcoholism when they grow up. It is this hope and this quickening that augur well for lowering the number of people who are the casualties of alcoholism. If the prophecy holds true, the need for a book like this will no longer exist for future generations.

BIBLIOGRAPHIC NOTES

CHAPTER 1 INTRODUCTION
Page 4 The two reviews are: E. H. Sutherland, H. G. Schroeder, and C. L. Tordella, "Personality Traits and the Alcoholic," *Quarterly Journal of Studies on Alcohol,* 11: 547–561, 1950, and L. Syme, "Personality Characteristics and the Alcoholic, A Critique of Current Studies," *Quarterly Journal of Studies on Alcohol,* 18: 288–302, 1957. As an antidote to these reviews, the reader is referred to J. D. Armstrong, "The Search for the Alcoholic Personality," *Annals of the American Academy of Political and Social Science,* 315: 40–47, 1958.

Page 8 Concise summaries of the major contemporary personality theories may be found in *Theories of Personality,* by C. H. Hall and G. Lindzey, Wiley, New York, 1965. Definitional problems are discussed by G. Allport in *Personality, A Psychological Interpretation,* Henry Holt, New York, 1937, and by G. Murphy in *Personality, A Biosocial Approach to Origins and Structure,* Harper, New York, 1947.

Pages 8–9 Definitional problems with regard to alcoholism have been discussed and summarized by E. Jellinek in *The Disease Concept of Alcoholism,* Hillhouse, Highland Park, N.J., 1960. The definition of alcoholism on page 9 comes from an article by M. Keller, "Alcoholism: Nature and Extent of the Problem," *Annals of the American Academy of Political and Social Science,* 315: 1–11, 1958.

Pages 10–11 The quotations about increasing female alcoholism are taken from an article by L. Shearer, "Women Who Drink Too Much," which appeared in *Parade* on January 22, 1967. A recent example of the evidence against a radical jump in women alcoholics may be found in: M. B. Bailey, P. W. Haberman, and H. Alksne, "The Epidemiology of Alcoholism in an Urban Residential Area," *Quarterly Journal of Studies on Alcohol,* 26: 19–40, 1965.

CHAPTER 2 DEPENDENCY AND MASCULINITY
Page 13 Reports of studies of institutionalized infants may be found in R. Spitz and K. M. Wolf, "Anaclitic Depression: An Inquiry into the Genesis of Psychiatric Conditions in Early Childhood," *Psychoanalytic Study of the Child,* 2: 313–342, 1946, and in J. Bowlby, *Maternal Care and*

BIBLIOGRAPHIC NOTES

Mental Health, World Health Association, 1952. H. F. Harlow summarized his experiments with infant monkeys in: "The Nature of Love," *American Psychologist,* 13: 673–685, 1958. A. Schaller described his field study of gorillas in *The Year of the Gorilla,* University of Chicago, Chicago, 1963.

Page 15 Technical descriptions of conflict over dependency wishes may be found in E. Lisansky, "The Etiology of Alcoholism: The Role of Psychological Predisposition," *Quarterly Journal of Studies on Alcohol,* 21: 314–343, 1960; and in W. McCord and J. McCord, *Origins of Alcoholism,* Stanford University, Stanford, California, 1960. The results of a study I did with my colleague, W. R. Meyers, casts doubt on some aspects of both formulations: H. T. Blane and W. R. Meyers, "Behavioral Dependence and Length of Stay in Psychotherapy Among Alcoholics," *Quarterly Journal of Studies on Alcohol,* 24: 503–510, 1963; some of the results of this study are described on pages 20–22.

CHAPTER 3 ANGER AND DEPRESSION

Page 46 Karl Menninger's formulation of the psychological make-up of alcoholics may be found in his book, *Man Against Himself,* Harcourt, Brace, New York, 1938.

CHAPTER 4 DENIAL

Page 55 A technical appraisal of the question of denial in relation to treatment may be found in a paper by R. A. Moore and T. C. Murphy, "Denial of Alcoholism as an Obstacle to Recovery," *Quarterly Journal of Studies on Alcohol,* 22: 597–609, 1961.

CHAPTER 8 THE ALCOHOLIC WOMAN

Page 115 Evidence bearing on the relation between personal crises and subsequent alcoholism in women is reviewed by B. A. Kinsey in *The Female Alcoholic: A Social Psychological Study,* Charles C. Thomas, Springfield, Illinois, 1966. Kinsey also summarizes what is known about the sexual behavior of women alcoholics.

Page 118 The study referred to is reported by F. J. Curran, "Personality Studies in Alcoholic Women," *Journal of Nervous and Mental Disease,* 86: 645–667, 1937.

Page 119 The studies on suicide among alcoholics are described in an article by E. G. Palola, T. L. Dorpat, and W. R. Larson, "Alcoholism and Suicidal Behavior," which appeared in *Society, Culture and Drinking Patterns,* D. J. Pittman and C. R. Snyder, eds., Wiley, New York, 1962, pp. 511–534.

CHAPTER 9 OUR RESPONSE TO ALCOHOLICS

Part of the material in this chapter is based on my paper, "Attitudes, Treatment, and Prevention," which appeared in *International Psychiatry Clinics,* 3(2): 103–126, 1966.

Page 121 The two decisions were handed down in the Driver (Driver v. Hinant, 356 F. 2d 761, 1966) and Easter (Easter v. District of Columbia, 209 A.2d 625, 1966) cases, which are described in *The Legal Issues in Alcoholism,* Boston University Law–Medicine Institute, Boston, 1966.

Page 122 E. M. Jellinek, *The Disease Concept of Alcoholism,* Hillhouse Press, Highland Park, N.J., 1960. The Iowa study is reported by H. A. Mulford and D. E. Miller, "Measuring Public Acceptance of the Alcoholic as a Sick Person," *Quarterly Journal of Studies on Alcohol,* 25: 314–323, 1964.

Page 123 These studies are: R. Straus, "Medical Practice and the Alcoholic," *Annals of the American Academy of Political and Social Science,* 315: 117–124, 1958; J. V. Sapir, "Social Work and Alcoholism," *Annals of the American Academy of Political and Social Science,* 315: 125–132, 1958; M. E. Chafetz and H. Demone, *Alcoholism and Society,* Oxford, New York, 1962; and E. X. Freed, "Opinions of Psychiatric Hospital Personnel and College Students Toward Alcoholism, Mental Illness, and Physical Disability," *Psychological Reports,* 15, 615–618, 1964.

Pages 123–27 The study on doctors' attitudes and behavior was reported in two parts: H. T. Blane, W. F. Overton, Jr., and M. E. Chafetz, "Social Factors in the Diagnosis of Alcoholism. I. Characteristics of the Patient," *Quarterly Journal of Studies on Alcohol,* 24:640–663, 1963; and I. Wolf, M. E. Chafetz, H. T. Blane, and M. J. Hill, "Social Factors in the Diagnosis of Alcoholism. II. Attitudes of Physicians," *Quarterly Journal of Studies on Alcohol,* 26: 72–79, 1965.

CHAPTER 10 TREATMENT AND ITS EFFECT

Page 134 The vitamin deficiency theory is propounded by R. J. Williams, "Alcoholics and Metabolism," *Scientific American,* 179: 50–53, 1948. A devastating criticism of the theory has been made by D. Lester, "Self-selection of Alcohol by Animals, Human Variation, and the Etiology of Alcoholism: A Critical Review," *Quarterly Journal of Studies on Alcohol,* 27: 395–438, 1966.

Page 146 The study on motivation is reported by M. E. Chafetz, *et al.* "Establishing Treatment Relations with Alcoholics," *Journal of Nervous and Mental Disease,* 134: 395–409, 1962. Research evaluating psychotherapy with alcoholics has been reviewed by M. J. Hill and H. T. Blane, "Evaluation of Psychotherapy with Alcoholics; A Critical Review," *Quarterly Journal of Studies on Alcohol,* 28: 76–104, 1967.

CHAPTER 11 PREVENTING ALCOHOLISM

Some of the material in this chapter is based on a paper, "Trends in the Prevention of Alcoholism" that I read at the 1966 annual meeting of the American Association for the Advancement of Science.

Page 152 This study is reported by A. F. Williams, H. Unterberger, and L. DiCicco.

Page 153 The views of M. E. Chafetz may be found in "Alcohol Excess," *Annals of the New York Academy of Political and Social Science,* 133: 808–813, 1966.

Page 155 R. Lindner discussed the romance of alcohol in "Alcoholism and Crime," *Alcohol Hygiene,* 1: 6, 1945.

Page 157 Injured-while-drinking students are described by G. L. Maddox in "Teen-agers and Alcohol," *Annals of the New York Academy of Political and Social Science,* 133: 856–865, 1966.

INDEX

Accidental injuries, alcoholism and, 157, 158
Accomplishments, real or illusory, focus on, 85
Adequacy, sense of, 85, 111
Aggrandizement, attitude of, 84
Aggression, 35, 37, 38, 45, 108
  socialization of, 63
Alcohol
  dependence on, 14, 18
  myths concerning, 155–56
"Alcohol education" programs, 151
Alcoholics, anger of, *see* Anger
  childish behavior of, 71
  children of, 157
  civil liberties and, 121
  commitment of, 76
  counterdependent, *see* Counterdependent alcoholics
  denial by, *see* Denial
  dependency of, *see* Dependency
  dependent, *see* Dependent alcoholic
  dependent-independent, *see* Dependent-independent alcoholic
  depression of, *see* Depression
  dislike and derision of, 128–33
  frustration of, *see* Frustration
  imperfect socialization of, 64
  impulsivity of, *see* Impulsivity
  independent, 18, 19
  job-seeking tendencies of unemployed, 88–89
  lone drinker, 96–97
  masculinity of, 13–34
  number of, estimating, 11–12

over-evaluation of self by, *see* Over-evaluation of self
  parents of, 81
  professional attitudes toward, 122–133
  public attitudes toward, 122–33
  referral of, 58–59, 124, 127
  relationships of, 92–106
    with therapist, 99–106
    with women therapists, 104–06
  response to, 120–33
  rules and regulations, keeping of, 75–76
  siding with, 43–44
  skid-row, 124, 125
  sociability of, 95–96
  social connections, emphasis of, 84
  suicides among, 118–19
  treatment of, *see* Treatment
  under-evaluation of self by, *see* Under-evaluation of self
  women, *see* Women alcoholics
Alcoholics Anonymous, 53, 58, 69, 88–89, 140, 143–44
Alcoholism
  attitude toward, 120–22
  causes of, 6
  definition of, 8–10
  denial in, 49–61
  diagnosis of, hesitancy in, 125–27
  illness of, 121, 123
  impulse disorder, 62
  prevention of, 148–59, 164
  public health problem, 121
  self-destructiveness of, 46
  sex ratios for, 11

169

Allport, Gordon, 8
Anger, 35–46, 114, 131, 133, 160
  comradeship in, 41–42
  depression and, 39–40
  forms of, 41–42, 43
  frustration and, 66
  handling of, 40–42
  toward authority, 67–69
Antabuse, treatment with, 134
Anxiety, 62, 81, 129, 130, 160, 161
Apomorphine, treatment with, 135,
  142
Assault, physical, 38, 40
Attention, attempts to obtain, 81, 82,
  83
Authority
  anger toward, 67–69
  counterdependent alcoholic's view
  of, 70
Aversion therapy, 135, 142

Badness, sense of, 80
Behavior therapy, 142–43
Biological dependence, 13
Breakdown of denial, 47, 55, 56, 57,
  61
Brief psychotherapy, 136, 137
Burroughs, William S., 120

Career women, 111–12
Casework, 136, 137–39
Chafetz, Morris, 153–54
Chemotherapies, 134–35
Childlike behavior of alcoholics, 71
Children of alcoholics, 157
Civil liberties, alcoholics and, 121
Clergymen, see Pastoral counselors
Clinic, alcohol
  referral to, 58–59
  treatment in, 59–60
Collegiate drinking behavior, 157
Comic strip series, alcoholics por-
  trayed in, 1
Commitment of alcoholic, 76
Community Mental Health Center
  Act (1963), 151
Comprehensive-treatment plan, 135
Compulsive eating, 62

Comradeship-in-anger, 41–42
Conflict, 160
Conscious control, 82
  admission of inability for, aversion to, 50
"Controlled" drinking, 73
Counseling, 136
Counselors, 89
  dehumanizing relationship during
  treatment, 102–04
  exalting the relationship during
  treatment, 100–01
  pastoral, 28–29, 60, 132
  relations with, 99
  relations with alcoholics, 99–106
  women, relations of alcoholics
  with, 104–06
Counterdependent alcoholic, 18–20,
  160
  anger of, 36
  forms of, 41–42, 43
  handling of, 40–42
  treatment of, 42–44
  authority as viewed by, 70
  denial by, 52, 53–55, 56, 60, 61
  frustration of, 66, 69–71
  impulsiveness of, 66, 69–71
  intensity of dependency, fear of,
  42
  job-seeking tendencies of unemployed, 88, 89
  over- and under-evaluation of self
  by, 84–86, 91
  treatment of, 87–90
  relationships of, 99
  sociability of, 95–96
  treatment of, 26–30
Court decisions concerning alcoholics, 121–22
Crime, alcohol an extenuating circumstance in, 130

Danger, reaction to, 35
Days of Wine and Roses (Miller),
  1
Dehumanizing the therapist relationship during treatment, 102–
  104

Delinquents, drinking behavior of,
 158
Delusions, 53
Denial, 47–61, 81, 161
 breakdown of, 47, 55, 56, 57, 61
 meaning of, 47
 minimal, 55
 normal, 48, 51, 61
 psychotic, 48, 51, 53, 61
 treatment and, 55–61
 types of, 48–50
Dependence
 biological, 13
 mutual, 92
 on alcohol, 14, 18
 psychological, 13, 14
Dependency, 36, 83, 160, 161
 aggression and anger secondary
  to, 45–46
 frustration of, 36
 intensity of, fear of, 42
 in the infant, 64
 masculinity and, 13–34
 surrender to, 16–17
 women alcoholics, 107–10
Dependency crisis, reaction to, 57
Dependency needs, 14, 15, 16, 18,
  20, 77, 90
 frustration of, 39
 satisfaction of, 64–65
 women alcoholics, 107–09
Dependent alcoholic, 16–17, 20, 160
 anger of, 36
  forms of, 41–42, 43
  handling of, 40–42
  treatment of, 42–44
 denial by, 52–53, 56, 61
 frustration of, 66–69
 impulsiveness of, 66–69
 job-seeking tendencies of unemployed, 88–89
 over- and under-evaluation of self
  by, 81–84, 85, 91
  treatment of, 87–90
 problems of, 24–25
 rehabilitation of, 25–26
 relationships and, 97, 98, 99
 treatment of, 22–25
 women, 109–10

Dependent drives, socialization of,
 63
Dependent-independent alcoholic,
 20–21, 160
 anger of, 36
  forms of, 41–42, 43
  handling of, 40–42
  treatment of, 42–44
 denial by, 52, 55, 56, 61
 frustration of, 66, 71–73
 impulsiveness of, 66, 71–73
 intensity of dependency, fear of,
  42
 over- and under-evaluation of self
  by, 87, 91
  treatment of, 87–90
 relationships and, 98–99
 sociability of, 95
 treatment of, 30–33
Dependent wishes, 15–16, 36
Depression, 39–40, 79, 111–12, 160
 suicidal, 39
 treatment of, 42, 44–45
Deprivation, 81
Diagnosis of alcoholism, hesitancy
 in, 125–27
Drifters, alcoholic, 16
Drugs, treatment with, 134–35, 142
Duress, consultation under, 60–61

Eating behavior, socialization of, 63
Eighteenth Amendment, 151
Emetine, treatment with, 135
Emotional disorders, treatment of,
 142
"Experts-together" relationship dur-
 ing treatment, 101–02

Failure, fear of, 86
Fear, 66
 of dependent relation, 70
 of failure, 86
 of trust, 100
Federal government, role of, 121–
 122
Freud, Sigmund, 8, 35, 71
Frustration, 35–36, 39, 64–77, 80,
 90, 161

INDEX

About the Author

Howard T. Blane was graduated *cum laude* in 1950 from Harvard and went on to the Clark University for his M.A. and Ph.D. In 1954, he was Clinical Research Psychologist at the Children's Hospital in Boston. In 1956, he became associated with Massachusetts General Hospital where he is now a psychologist. He is also Assistant Clinical Professor of Psychology at Harvard Medical School.

Professor Blane lives in Boston with his wife and two children.

73 10 9 8 7 6 5 4 3

(continued from front flap)

Dr. Blane raises two primary questions: What is the core issue for most alcoholics? How do they resolve the conflict? In answering these questions, Dr. Blane uses the concept of dependency as his basis.

In discussing the personality traits of alcoholics in relation to dependency needs and wishes, he shows how an understanding of the origins of these traits can be used in helping alcoholics. Dr. Blane stresses that self-destructive, provocative actions should not obscure the fact that the alcoholic is a sick person, wanting help, but afraid to seek and ask for it. Continuity and consistency of care, respect for individual integrity and dignity, and awakening desires for health are essential for successful and healing relationships with alcoholics.

The book is directed to all those who work directly or peripherally with alcoholics, in addition to the wives, parents, children, and other relatives of alcoholics. It should be helpful to physicians, nurses, psychologists, social workers, clergymen, personnel officers, policemen, correctional workers, welfare officials, and the problem drinker himself.

Here is an understanding of the ways in which alcoholics behave and the reasons behind these ways of behavior.

The author, Howard T. Blane, is the Director of Research of the Preventive Intervention Study within the Department of Psychiatry of Massachusetts General Hospital.